THE PARENT ADVENTURE

PREPARING YOUR KID FOR A LIFE WITH GOD

RODNEY & SELMA WILSON

LifeWay Press®
Nashville, Tennessee

ISBN 978-1-4158-6645-0
Item 005181385

Dewey decimal classification: 649
Subject heading: PARENTING

This book is the resource for course 1424 in the subject area
Personal Life in the Christian Growth Study Plan.

Unless indicated otherwise, Scripture quotations are taken from the Holman
Christian Standard Bible®, copyright © 1999, 2000, 2002, 2003 by Holman Bible Publishers.
Used by permission. Scripture quotations marked NIV are taken
from the Holy Bible, New International Version, copyright © 1973, 1978, 1984
by International Bible Society. Scripture quotations marked *The Message* are taken
from Eugene H. Peterson, *The Message* (Colorado Springs: NavPress, 1995).

To order additional copies of this resource, write to LifeWay Church Resources
Customer Service; One LifeWay Plaza; Nashville, TN 37234-0113;
fax (615) 251-5933; phone toll free (800) 458-2772; e-mail *orderentry@lifeway.com;*
order online at *www.lifeway.com;* or visit the LifeWay Christian Store serving you.

Printed in the United States of America

Leadership and Adult Publishing
LifeWay Church Resources
One LifeWay Plaza
Nashville, TN 37234-0175

CONTENTS

RODNEY &SELMA WILSON

THE AUTHORS

Married for 32 years, Rodney and Selma have two adult daughters and one son-in-law. Rodney has served as a youth minister, a campus minister, and a collegiate missions director. For the past 10 years he has been the marriage and family minister at First Baptist Church in Smyrna, Tennessee.

Selma has served as a ministry partner with Rodney over the years, as well as a teacher, social worker, and marriage and family consultant. For the past 14 years she has served through the ministry of LifeWay Christian Resources as women's ministry was launched and currently serves as the associate vice-president of Church Resources at LifeWay.

Rodney and Selma have been actively involved in marriage and family ministry for most of their married life, teaching, speaking, writing, and counseling to build strong marriages and families as God designed. They have been actively involved with *HomeLife* magazine for the past 10 years as contributors and recently served for 5 years as executive editors. They are the authors of *Extraordinary Marriage* and national speakers for Festivals of Marriage. Their mission is to help marriages and families reach their full potential in Jesus Christ.

ACKNOWLEDGMENTS

Our parents, Roy and Juanita Rymer and J. B. and Eudy Wilson. Thanks for loving God, loving each other, loving us, and loving the church. The security of that love gave us wings to fly!

Our kids, Natalie and Jennifer, and our son-in-law, David. Thanks for giving us the joy of experiencing the parent adventure. We are better people because you are in our lives. What fun we are having as we watch you run after God and experience your own adventures with Him!

The team at LifeWay:

- Bill Craig, the director of Leadership and Adult Ministry, Church Resources, who had the original vision for this project and the faith in us to deliver the message
- LifeWay Research team—Scott McConnell and Ed Stetzer
- Chris Johnson, the editor-in-chief for this project, and David Haney, editor, who helped make our words clearer
- Jon Rodda, our designer, who delivered the visuals for this message
- Rick Simms and Debbie Beavers, our video-production team
- The team at B&H Publishers, Thomas Walters, and Judi Hayes, who did a great job capturing this message for all parents

Pat Hood, the senior pastor of First Baptist Church in Smyrna, Tennessee. Your vision for having a marriage and family-enrichment ministry at our church provided us the laboratory to test many of these parenting ideas.

A special thanks goes to our daughter, Jennifer McCaman, for going on this journey with us, using her amazing talents as a writer and an editor to make our message stronger and clearer (and for the many times she sat down and said, "That is not going in the book!"). Thanks to Jennifer and Natalie for reading this book and making sure all we remembered in our parent adventure was indeed true and accurate.

Most of all, we thank God for the abundant, extraordinary life He has given us through Jesus Christ. Every day is indeed an adventure as we experience the wonder of being children of God! For His grace and mercy that are fresh every morning. For the daily security that our future is solid as we run the race to pursue Christ until the day when we begin the ultimate adventure of an eternity with Him! We pray that all who complete this study will know Christ fully and experience the abundant, beyond-common life that is available to all who call Him Savior and Lord.

INTRODUCTION

Welcome to *The Parent Adventure: Preparing Your Kid for Life with God*. Our purpose is to introduce you to concepts of parenting that will benefit you and your children on the journey of parenting. We had you in mind as we developed this resource. Our research shows that you are busy juggling the responsibilities of surviving day to day. Most parents never take on the challenge of reading a resource on parenting because they don't have time.

The best way to complete this material is to join other parents for a seven-week group study. Suggestions for the small-group experience, provided at the beginning of each chapter, are designed to be casual and easy to use. The small-group sessions are discussion based, suggesting questions that prompt conversation among participants. In the group session you will also view DVD segments featuring the authors as they introduce the topic for the session and offer real-life examples and experiences to stimulate discussion. The DVDs, along with a copy of this member book and a copy of *The Parent Adventure* trade book, are included in *The Parent Adventure Leader Kit* (item 005126524).

After attending the small-group session, you will want to read the corresponding chapter in this book, which reinforces the topic that was introduced in your small-group experience. The workbook format allows you to interact with the content and make observations about what you discover in the process of your weekly parent adventure. The chapters are easy to read and give you freedom to work through the information at your own pace. The writing style is intentionally conversational so that you feel you are in dialogue with the authors. You will discover that the content is biblically based, providing you a strong scriptural foundation for your parent adventure.

THE
ADVENTURE
BEGINS

chapter one

session one GROUP EXPERIENCE

GET TO KNOW YOUR GROUP

SHARE how many children you have, their ages, and some information about each one.

PRAY, asking the Lord to teach the group to be better parents who intentionally and diligently equip their children for life with God.

WARM-UP

- What is the best thing you like about parenting?

- What is most challenging for you about parenting?

- What surprises you the most about parenting?

WATCH DVD

- Watch DVD session 1.
- What stood out to you in this session?

THE BIBLICAL VIEW

Psalm 139:13-14

"It was You who created my inward parts; You knit me together in my mother's womb. I will praise You, because I have been remarkably and wonderfully made. Your works are wonderful, and I know this very well."

- How does knowing that God created you and your child affect your view of parenting?

Deuteronomy 6:5-7

"Love the LORD your God with all your heart, with all your soul, and with all your strength. These words that I am giving you today are to be in your heart. Repeat them to your children. Talk about them when you sit in your house and when you walk along the road, when you lie down and when you get up."

- What do these verses teach about the purpose of parenting?

- What actions are parents to take with their children?

John 10:10

"A thief comes only to steal and to kill and to destroy. I have come that they may have life and have it in abundance."

- What would abundant life look like for a parent today?

- How does it feel to know that God wants an abundant life for you right now, in the midst of the challenges of parenthood?

Matthew 7:9-11

"What man among you, if his son asks him for bread, will give him a stone? Or if he asks for a fish, will give him a snake? If you then, who are evil, know how to give good gifts to your children, how much more will your Father in heaven give good things to those who ask Him!"

- You want the best for your kids. What are some specific things you want for your children?

- How does it make you feel when you discover that just like a father who gives good things to his children, God gives good things to those who ask?

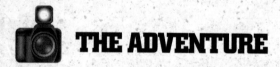 **THE ADVENTURE**

- Brainstorm thoughts that come to mind when you hear the word *adventure*.

- Briefly share a memorable adventure you've had with your spouse.

- Do you see parenting as an adventure? In what ways?

CLOSING THOUGHTS

- Parents are to pass the baton of faith to their children. Use the course overview on pages 24–25 to point out ways this study will help equip you for that task.

- Turn to "The Parent Adventure Plan" on page 26. Identify which verses from this chapter you will share with your children.

- Close the session with prayer.

NEXT WEEK

- Read chapter 1 and complete the learning activities before the next session.

- Bring to the next session a precious artifact from your children's past, such as a photo, blanket, handprint, stuffed animal, or drawing.

Deuteronomy 6:5-7

"Love the LORD your God with all your heart, with all your soul, and with all your strength. These words that I am giving you today are to be in your heart. Repeat them to your children. Talk about them when you sit in your house and when you walk along the road, when you lie down and when you get up."

Twenty-seven hours. That's how long Selma was in labor before Jenny was in our arms. Twenty-seven long hours. That's tough on a dad. (I guess Selma did some of the work too.) The doctor placed Jenny in our arms, and our lives were changed forever. She was our daughter, a part of us. We laughed and cried at the same time. Nothing could have prepared us for the moment when we realized that we were officially parents. It was as if time stood still.

Recall when you first held your child. What emotions did you experience?

Within the next 24 hours I was captivated by the reality that I was a dad. Future responsibilities weighed heavily on my heart. Could I protect Jenny from the world? Clearly, I would need to build a wall around our house to keep the boys out. No guy would ever be good enough for my little girl!

What concerns did you first experience as a parent?

Before Jenny was born, we read everything we could find on parenting, raising a newborn, and starting a family. We talked to friends and worked in the church nursery. But we quickly learned that nothing could fully prepare us for the parenting experience.

Now, after launching our own children from the home and spending more than 20 years ministering to families—caring for newborns, guiding preadolescents, raising teenagers, and launching young adults into the world—only one word captures the whole experience—*adventure!* Adventure implies both danger and excitement, and all parents know that parenting is a little of both. Of all we will accomplish in this life, other than accepting Christ as Savior, there is no greater blessing, no greater joy, and no greater adventure than being parents.

Check the word that best describes the way you view parenting.

☐ Nightmare   ☐ Rat race   ☐ Endurance test
☐ Adventure   ☐ Drudgery   ☐ Rollercoaster ride

Explain in your own words why parenting is so important.

A GIFT FROM GOD

Like all great adventures, the parenting journey comes bundled with excitement, expectation, anxiety, stress, and exhaustion. For many, parenting is an incredibly intimidating concept. It's tempting to take a survival approach and just hold your breath, hoping your children are healthy when they're born and praying they don't give you as much trouble as the kids in the horror stories you've heard.

It might seem that parents roll the dice and randomly get their kids. In reality, chance has no role in your parent adventure. God chose to give you the kids you have, and He doesn't make mistakes. God is the Creator and Giver of life. He created you, and He created your child. Your kids are indeed wonderfully made. No accidents. No mistakes. God designed them for purpose and meaning in life.

This is how the psalmist put it:

Psalm 139:13-16, The Message
"Oh yes, you shaped me first inside, then out;
you formed me in my mother's womb.
I thank you, High God—you're breathtaking!
Body and soul, I am marvelously made!
I worship in adoration—what a creation!
You know me inside and out,
you know every bone in my body;
You know exactly how I was made, bit by bit,
how I was sculpted from nothing into something.
Like an open book, you watched me grow from conception to birth;
all the stages of my life were spread out before you,
The days of my life all prepared
before I'd even lived one day."

Reread this passage with your children in mind. List specific attributes of your children that confirm God's intricate involvement in their development.

How does knowing that God created you and your child affect your view of parenting?

THE PURPOSE OF PARENTING

All great adventures have a destination. Whether athletes are hiking, running, sailing, or biking, they need to know the goal of the trip, the purpose and mission of the journey. God's Word clearly defines our goal as parents.

Deuteronomy 6:5-7

"Love the LORD your God with all your heart, with all your soul, and with all your strength. These words that I am giving you today are to be in your heart. Repeat them to your children. Talk about them when you sit in your house and when you walk along the road, when you lie down and when you get up."

According to these verses, what is your main purpose as a parent?

What is God able to do through you as a parent?

In the passage underline the ways parents are to teach God's Word to their children.

As this passage teaches, parents are responsible for connecting their children to God. The greatest thing you can give your children is a love for God and an understanding that all of life is about Him. As a parent, you have the privilege to introduce your children to God and to model what it looks like to follow Him in the everyday experiences of life. Parenting is a gift from God, a gift that ultimately centers on Him. You have the opportunity to touch the future. Through your child you can influence, encourage, and bless the next generation. Everything else you'll accomplish as a parent should spring from this purpose.

That doesn't mean families have to retreat from the world and spend every waking moment reading the Bible and singing hymns. We want to show you how to bring the truth of God into your everyday home, in the middle of busy 21st-century life. We want to show you how to create an environment for your children to know God, own their own faith, and spend their lives making God known.

Deuteronomy 6:5-7 will serve as our focal verses for this study, anchoring us to our main purpose as Christian parents. These verses emphasize the importance of a parent's relationship with God. Parents need to have a love relationship with God that consumes our lives (heart, soul, and strength). If we have that kind of relationship with God, we will know Him personally and intimately, and we will seek to learn the ways of God through His Word.

As you begin this study, it is vitally important to make sure you have a personal relationship with God.

As you read the following outline, prayerfully consider whether you have taken each necessary step to know God personally.

1. Acknowledge your need for God: "All have sinned and fall short of the glory of God" (Rom. 3:23).
2. Believe that God's love for you provided a way to overcome your need: "God proves His own love for us in that while we were still sinners Christ died for us!" (Rom. 5:8).
3. Accept the truth of God's love through Christ: "The wages of sin is death, but the gift of God is eternal life in Christ Jesus our Lord" (Rom. 6:23).
4. Confess Jesus as Lord: "If you confess with your mouth, 'Jesus is Lord,' and believe in your heart that God raised Him from the dead, you will be saved" (Rom. 10:9).

The parent adventure begins by realizing that God loves you so much that He gave His only Son, Jesus, to die for you! When you accept this gift, when you grasp the reality of your need and the ultimate sacrifice He made to demonstrate His love for you, then you can love God with all your heart, soul, and strength.

If you have not experienced the gift of eternal life through Christ but would like to do that now, pray a prayer similar to the following. Feel free to use your own words to express your thoughts.

> *Dear God, I know I am a sinner. I believe Jesus died to save me from my sins. I ask for Your forgiveness, and I accept Your offer of eternal life through Jesus Christ. Thank You for forgiving me of my sins. From this day forward I choose to follow You and to call You the Lord of my life. Amen.*

If you prayed to receive Christ, congratulations and welcome to the family of God! Share this decision with your spouse, a local-church minister, a Christian friend, or your Sunday School teacher or small-group leader. Connect with a church that can help you grow in your faith.

Maybe you have already embraced Christ as your Savior and Lord; but as you begin this study, you want to reaffirm your love for Him. Take time to do that now. Ask Him to help you learn how to be a parent who leads his or her children to follow Him.

Because of a parent's responsibility to lead his or her children to know God, it is important for every parent participating in *The Parent Adventure* to be in a personal love relationship with God through Jesus Christ, His Son. We want to help you see the need—and show you how—to deeply involve God in the great adventure of parenting.

STRENGTH FOR THE JOURNEY

If you've ever stepped back as a parent and thought, *I really have no idea what I'm doing,* you're certainly not alone. That's when we have to depend on God. I once heard a pastor friend say that when we are out on a limb with no way to make it on our own, that is right where God wants us. It's where He can do His best work, because we are ready to acknowledge our total need for Him.

Parenting places us out on that limb. Thankfully, God doesn't leave us to fend for ourselves. He assures us in His Word of His willingness to lead in our lives if we let Him. In the Book of John, for example, Jesus told us that He is the Good Shepherd and that He came to give us a full, meaningful, beyond-common life.

John 10:10
"I have come that they may have life and have it in abundance."

How does Jesus' promise of abundant life apply to your parenting experience?
☐ I experience His blessings all the time.
☐ It's hard to see the connection.

Explain why you answered the way you did.

Sometimes those persistent, iron-strong three-year-olds or teenagers with tongues of steel make it easy to believe we are exempt from John 10:10. Understand that God doesn't call a John 10:10 timeout for parents of adolescents. He is not laughing and thinking, *Maybe when they get those rowdy kids out of the house, then they can experience life.* You can experience abundant life right where you are. Right *when* you are. Right in the middle and throughout whatever passage of life we are triumphing over or suffering through—including parenting kids of various ages and unique personalities.

Newsflash: Parenting isn't for the faint of heart. Nor is the perfect parent adventure going to be handed to you. God never promised that any part of life would be easy or struggle-free. Even in the middle of challenges, however, we can experience the promises of God's Word—His love and His desire for us to experience life fully. If you are a Christ-follower, John 10:10 will always apply to you. We must choose daily to live that abundant life. It's never forced on us.

MAKING TIME

Understand up front that the parent adventure requires one of your most precious resources—your time. Nothing and no one can substitute for the time required to invest in your children. You can't delegate this task to your church, pastor, youth minister, grandparents, friends, Christian school, or anyone else. All of these can help, but the principal job is yours.

What does spending time with your kids communicate to them?

Time given to your child says:
- "I love you, period. Not because of what you do but because of who you are."
- "I am for you."
- "I believe in you."
- "You matter to me."
- "I'll get you ready for the future."
- "I'll teach you about God."

The parent adventure requires making time to introduce your kids to God and His ways.

Think about the time you spend teaching your kids about God. Is the amount of time ☐ adequate? ☐ inadequate?

If you need to spend more time with your kids, what adjustments do you need to make to do so?

PASSING THE BATON

When I was in high school, I ran the men's 4x100 relay for our track team. Each member of the team carried the baton, ran one hundred yards, then passed it to the next team member.

One year we were heavily favored to win the gold in the state meet. We were invincible. We could taste victory. All we had to do was qualify for the finals in heats earlier in the day. This was cake, easy for the fastest team in the state. I ran my 100 leg, passed the baton to my teammate, and was putting on my warm-ups when I heard an unusual sound—a corporate sigh from the stands. Then those who ran against me started saying how sorry they were for our school. Our third and fourth runners had dropped the baton during the exchange. Our season was over just like that.

After our track team dropped the baton, it didn't matter how fast we ran. As a parent, it doesn't matter how much money you make, what kind of car you drive, how much education you receive, your corporate position, or how much you have in your 401(k) or stock portfolio. If you fail to teach your kids about God and His plans for their lives, you are running in vain.

We parents have a responsibility to pass our faith baton to the next generation. We must do our part to prepare our kids for their unique adventure with God. It is our job to pass the baton of faith to our children. This study will help you find practical ways to do so by creating a home environment in which your children can learn about God through the day-to-day stuff of life.

One biblical concept of parenting comes from an unlikely source. John 4 tells the account of the Samaritan woman at the well. Jesus talks with her; and she comes to believe that He is truly the Messiah, placing her trust in Him. Then she goes back to her town and tells everyone she has found the Messiah. Later, after Jesus talks to the townspeople in person, they make this incredible statement to the woman: "We no longer believe because of what you said, for we have heard for ourselves and know that this really is the Savior of the world" (v. 42).

As parents, it is our role, like the Samaritan woman, to tell our kids about Jesus, passing along the baton of our faith. We ultimately want our kids to react like the townspeople: "Mom, Dad, I no longer believe because of what you have told me. You told me about Christ and modeled Him for me; but I have heard, seen, and experienced Christ for myself and now know that He really is the Savior of the world." This is passing the baton!

Check the situation that applies to you.

- ☐ First-generation Christian: I have the baton of faith ready to pass to my children.
- ☐ Second-generation Christian: my parents passed the baton of faith to me, and I am ready to pass it to my children.
- ☐ Multiple-generation Christian: several generations of believers have passed down the baton of faith, and I am ready to pass it to my children.
- ☐ I am not yet a Christian.

THE BEST FOR YOUR KIDS

All parents want good things for their children.

Check the things you want for your children.

- ☐ Straight A's
- ☐ College education
- ☐ College scholarship
- ☐ Healthy friendships
- ☐ Financial stability
- ☐ Common sense
- ☐ Favor with teachers
- ☐ Proficient reader
- ☐ Strong work ethic
- ☐ Stable job
- ☐ Valedictorian
- ☐ Strong athlete
- ☐ Accomplished musician
- ☐ Vibrant Christian
- ☐ Active church member
- ☐ Servant to others
- ☐ Spiritual leader
- ☐ Faithful husband/wife
- ☐ Great parent
- ☐ Other:

Guess what? God wants the best for your kids too:

Matthew 7:9-11

"What man among you, if his son asks for bread, will give him a stone? Or if he asks for a fish, will give him a snake? If you, then, who are evil, know how to give good gifts to your children, how much more will your Father in heaven give good things to those who ask Him!"

Above everything else we want for our kids, we must give them the truth of God. His extraordinary plans for our children will far exceed even the best plans we make for them.

LEADING THE WAY

Research in the fields of psychology and sociology points to the critical role parents play in the lives of their children. Here are few examples.

- A study from Okrent revealed that 83 percent of teens trust what their parents say over their teachers, friends, and the media.[1]
- Author John Bruhn states, "Nothing is more likely to produce a happy, well-adjusted child than a loving family."[2]
- MTV research found that youth are happiest when they're with their families.[3]
- In a LifeWay research project, 25 percent of parents rated their parental fulfillment as excellent in their families, and another 68 percent said it was very good or good.[4]

But LifeWay research also found two very troubling indicators in American families today: only 14 percent of parents indicate they are very familiar with what the Bible has to say about parenting, and only 9 percent define success in parenting to include faith in God.[5] While research clearly shows that parents play a significant role in our children's future, it also shows that preparing our children for life with God is missing from 21st-century parenting.

"[In] the end, the negative aspects of being a parent—
the loss of intimacy, the expense, the total lack of free
time, the incredible burden of responsibility, the constant
nagging fear of having done the wrong thing, et cetera—
are more than outweighed by the positive
aspects, such as never again lacking
for primitive drawings to attach to
your refrigerator with magnets."[6]
—Dave Barry

As parents, we often want a formula. Many parents think, *Give me five things to do that will guarantee this parenting thing will be a success. I want the simple, condensed version that promises my child will always be safe and have a happy, successful life.* There's isn't a formula that will guarantee the success of your parenting experience and the success of your child. But you can be 100 percent confident in God! He is the only guarantee, the only promise for all of life. No matter what the future holds, God knows the future. Preparing your child for life with God—this is the parent adventure.

Yes, following God is exciting, challenging, rewarding, and dangerous at times. Some of the danger in the parent adventure lies in the risk, the fact that we cannot control how our children will respond to our leadership. Take the parable of the prodigal son that Jesus told.

Review the parable of the prodigal son in Luke 15:11-31. What do you learn about God from this story that gives you confidence in parenting?

Same dad, two sons. One stayed home and obeyed all the rules, while the other flat-out rebelled against Dad, took off, and went wild. We never want our children to rebel against God or us. But the good news is that God, our Heavenly Father, is always working and waiting for us to return home to Him (see Luke 15:20). He is able to redeem the mistakes of our children—and our mistakes as parents—and use them for good.

Luke 15:20

"His father saw him and was filled with compassion, He ran, threw his arms around his neck, and kissed him."

Proverbs 22:6

"Teach a youth about the way he should go; even when he is old, he will not depart from it."

Our job as parents is to teach our children the ways of God, to which they will remain faithful throughout their lives (see Prov. 22:6). They, like many of us, will not always make the best choices. But we can parent with confidence in God, in His love for us and our children, and in the promises of His Word.

BUILDING A LIFE

As three workers labored on a stone wall, someone walked up and asked each of them what they were doing. The first answered, "I am laying block." The second replied, "I am building a wall." But the third man proudly responded, "I am constructing a cathedral!"

Same wall. Same job. Same question. Entirely different perspectives on what they were trying to accomplish. One had a much bigger picture in mind.

In parenting we are doing much more than simply raising kids. We are touching the future. We are preparing our children for a lifetime adventure with God. We are impacting *their* children by the way we parent them. We are not merely laying parenting blocks. We are constructing cathedrals!

This cathedral-like construction of a kid into an adult can look intimidating at times, but it can be done—and it can be done *by you!* With God all things are possible (see Matt. 19:26). And with Him, parenting doesn't have to be a matter of mere survival. This can be one of the most exhilarating adventures of your life.

Matthew 19:26

"Jesus looked at them and said, 'With men this is impossible, but with God all things are possible.' "

Jesus used a building example in Matthew:

Matthew 7:24-27
"Everyone who hears these words of Mine and acts on them will be like a sensible man who built his house on the rock. The rain fell, the rivers rose, and the winds blew and pounded that house. Yet it didn't collapse, because its foundation was on the rock. But everyone who hears these words of Mine and doesn't act on them will be like a foolish man who built his house on the sand. The rain fell, the rivers rose, the winds blew and pounded that house, and it collapsed. And its collapse was great!"

What is the foundation Jesus referred to?
☐ Solid rock ☐ Jesus Himself ☐ Wisdom

The Parent Adventure will help equip you to prepare your child for a life with God that is built on the only solid foundation—Jesus Christ. That foundation will stand throughout all eternity!

Stop and pray for God's wisdom and guidance in building your children's lives on the foundation of Jesus.

Here is an overview of the areas you will examine in this study to prepare your kids for life with God.

Chapter 2
"Letting Go" explores the truth that your child belongs to God. You can parent every day through every stage of your children's lives with a confident understanding that you are to let them go to experience their own adventures with God.

Chapter 3
"A Yes Home" shows how you can create a home where your children can grow, learn, create, and experience the joy and wonder of life. There they will learn about a God who says yes, and they will ultimately say yes to Him.

Chapter 4
"Let's Talk" describes how sharing all of life together as a family and learning to openly share the experiences of life lay the foundation for your children to talk to God.

Chapter 5

"Pain Happens" helps you teach your child that pain is real for both parents and children, but God is always with us in and through the pain, working in our lives.

Chapter 6

"Celebrate!" prepares you to build a home that looks for God's blessings and regularly celebrates His work in the lives of parents and children as an act of worship.

FROM LIFEWAY RESEARCH

1/2 Only half of parents indicate that their religious faith plays an important role in their parenting.

Only 14 percent of parents indicate that they are very familiar with what the Bible has to say about parenting.

83% The vast majority of parents believe the parent or parents should be responsible for a child's spiritual development.

Only 12 percent of all parents said their religious faith is the top influence in how they raise their kids, with another 23 percent calling it one of the most important influences. Almost a third of all parents either had no religious faith or said it has little or no influence on their parenting.

Individuals who say they are more familiar with WHAT THE BIBLE SAYS on parenting are more likely to have a parenting plan. Individuals who are less familiar are less likely to have a parenting plan.

In general, PARENTS WHO HAVE A PLAN have more positive parenting experiences.[7]

At the end of each chapter we will suggest specific actions you and your kids can do together to apply what you have studied. We want you to join us on this journey. Let's explore some ways you can prepare your kids for life with God as we experience together what we call *The Parent Adventure*.

THE PARENT ADVENTURE PLAN

Look together at pictures or videos of the early years of your children's lives. Prepare a special meal or picnic on the living-room floor to celebrate the gift of being a parent. Let your children know how thankful you are that God has allowed you to be their parent.

Tell your children you are studying this book to be a better parent. If they are old enough, ask them to pray for you during this study.

Share one Scripture verse from this chapter with your children, letting them know what God's Word says about parenting.

PRAYER FOCUS

Each chapter will end with a prayer. We will offer one as a sample, but we encourage you to end your study of each chapter with a personal prayer.

Praying Paul's prayer below is a great way to begin our parent adventure together.

Ephesians 1:17-19
"I pray that the God of our Lord Jesus Christ, the glorious Father, would give you a spirit of wisdom and revelation in the knowledge of Him. I pray that the eyes of your heart may be enlightened so you may know what is the hope of His calling, what are the glorious riches of His inheritance among the saints, and what is the immeasurable greatness of His power to us who believe, according to the working of His vast strength."

LETTING GO

chapter two

session two GROUP EXPERIENCE

GET TO KNOW YOUR GROUP

DISCUSS what you discovered from your parent adventure after reading chapter 1, "The Adventure Begins."

SHARE a memory about one of your children, using the artifact you brought with you. If you lost all of your belongings, what keepsakes would you miss the most? Discuss reactions and feelings.

WARM-UP

- Describe the first time your child walked, swam, drove, rode a bike, studied, cooked, got dressed, or ate without your help.

- Share the fear and joy that came with the experience (for you and your child).

WATCH DVD

- Watch DVD session 2.
- What stood out to you in this session?

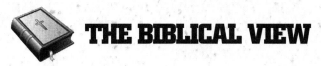 # THE BIBLICAL VIEW

Luke 2:46-50, The Message

"The next day [Mary and Joseph] found him in the Temple seated among the teachers, listening to them and asking questions. But his parents were not impressed; they were upset and hurt. His mother said, 'Young man, why have you done this to us? Your father and I have been half out of our minds looking for you.' He said, 'Why were you looking for me? Didn't you know that I had to be here, dealing with the things of my Father?' But they had no idea what he was talking about."

- How does it encourage you to know that Mary and Joseph also struggled with letting Jesus go?

Genesis 2:22,24

"The LORD God made a woman from the rib he had taken out of the man, and he brought her to the man. For this reason a man will leave his father and mother and be united to his wife, and they will become one flesh."

- What does this verse say about letting go?

- How can this passage extend beyond marriage?

Hebrews 13:5

"I will never leave you or forsake you."

- How does this verse empower you to let your children go with God?

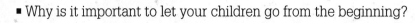

THE ADVENTURE

- Why is it important to let your children go from the beginning?

- Did your parents do a good job of letting you go? Explain.

- Why do many parents struggle with holding on too tightly?

- What is one way you can let your child go this week?

- Read the list on page 36 and name three qualities you want your child to have as an adult.

- How do you want your children to surpass you someday (financially, spiritually, educationally, relationally)?

- Your children belong to God. How does that fact change your perspective on parenting?

- How do you need God to specifically help you begin to let your children go?

- Review the ideas for letting go on pages 43–46. How might these ideas help you let go of your children at their particular stages of life?

CLOSING THOUGHTS

- Pray that you will see your role as a steward (not an owner) of your children.

- Ask God to help you let go every day to help your children grow into spiritually mature, independent followers of Christ.

- Pray that God will show you ways you hold on too tightly.

- Pray for your children to grow spiritually, socially, physically, emotionally, and intellectually for God's glory.

NEXT WEEK

Next week you will study "A Yes Home." You will learn to create an environment in which your children can grow, learn, and experience the joy of life while learning about a God who says yes.

LETTING GO

chapter two

Genesis 2:24
"For this reason a man will leave his father and mother."

Jennifer and I laughed all the way to school that morning. It was her first day of kindergarten, and I don't have to tell you who was more nervous (definitely Dad). Maybe that's because Jen was my oldest or maybe because neither of us knew how the departure from each other would go. So we laughed.

In the parking lot I prayed a brief prayer that God would protect her from … well, everything until Mom picked her up at 12:30 p.m.

I walked her down the hall until we found the classroom door. The rest was a scene straight out of Hollywood. The music faded, and the lights lowered. Jennifer's happy-go-lucky mood suddenly grew somber as she looked up at me and simply said, "Good-bye, Daddy."

I smiled, kissed her good-bye, and somehow made it to the car before I cried my way to work. I spent my entire 30-minute commute pondering the enormity of her words. Indeed it was good-bye. Good-bye to one chapter of parenting and hello to another.

Identify a time when you had to say a significant good-bye to one of your children. What chapters of his or her life were beginning and ending?

FACING THE GOOD-BYES

Jennifer's five-year-old wisdom made me realize that many more good-byes awaited us throughout the parenting adventure. My mind raced through elementary school, past the preteen and middle-school stages. I saw her standing in a cap and gown, graduating from high school, and moving away to college. Then … marriage? I was practically holding my grandchildren by the time I got to work. (It was an interesting ride to work that morning.)

As I pondered the end of several stages of our children's lives, one reality gripped me most: one day the hands-on dynamic of parenting my kids would end. One day I would no longer be the provider, protector, teacher, disciplinarian, and all-around predominant figure in my daughters' lives. The responsibility of raising Jennifer and Natalie was temporary. And this changed everything.

What emotions and thoughts did you experience when you said good-bye to your child?

That night I shared my experience with Selma. We began to pray and rethink our entire parenting experience. Instead of dreading the good-byes around every corner, we would use them to fuel our parenting. We determined to start with the end in mind, and the clock was ticking. Immediately, we would begin letting go a little each day to prepare our children for the day when they would leave us to embrace their own adventure with God. Letting go clearly meant getting our kids ready for life with God.

We hit our knees that night, recognizing our total dependence on God. We acknowledged that our girls belonged to the God who created them and knew the plans He had for them. When we got up off our knees, we were more confident in Him and more at peace with the unknown.

How did you react to the experience of saying good-bye to your child? In what ways did it change your parenting?

THE LETTING-GO LEAP

The idea of releasing your children into a cold, cruel world can be pretty scary. After all, you pour yourself into your offspring for nearly two decades. You give spiritually, emotionally, physically, and financially. You sacrifice so that they can have what you didn't. You put your social life and sometimes your career on hold to invest in their development. You are a 24-hour counselor, peacemaker, lawyer, doctor, teacher, teller, philosopher, clown, coach, mentor, maid, chauffeur, and more.

Then one day all of that ceases. Your role in parenting changes. The job you never really grasped in the first place is suddenly finished.

For a while it can seem like a small identity crisis. The momentary pain of letting go, however, is unquestionably necessary for your whole family. Watching your child soar toward adulthood, confident and secure in Christ, will bring incredible celebration.

Identify some causes for celebration when your children gain independence.

You can rejoice when your children leave the nest. They are now ready for their independent adventures with God. You will take on a different role in their lives, a very significant one but not the direct, hands-on role you once had. Don't forget; God has many more post–kid-raising adventures for you before your life on this earth ends. Maybe even grandparenting!

"It's not a parent's job to protect their kids from life, but to prepare them for it."[1]—*Actor Blake Segal*

I remember the first time I had to let go. It was our 10th wedding anniversary, and Rodney had planned a special celebration—a trip to New York City for just the two of us. Natalie was 18 months old at the time, and I had never left her. When Rodney let me know the trip was arranged, I had six weeks to get ready to let my girls go.

I cried; I prayed; I even fussed (to myself) at Rodney's insensitivity for making me leave them for three whole nights. Thankfully, we had dear friends whom I trusted with our girls, but there were still growing pains (mostly for Mom).

The big day of letting go came and went. As a young mother, I noticed that I was already developing some patterns of holding on too tightly, so the break was good for all of us. The girls survived—even thrived—while Rodney and I had a wonderful time celebrating our marriage, our ministry, and our children.

Leaving my girls for a few days was only the beginning. Here are some other milestones of letting go:

- Spending the night with friends
- The first overnight school trip
- The first boy-girl event
- The first youth mission trip
- The first time they drive alone
- The first day of their first job
- The first mission trip overseas

In the previous list, place a check mark beside letting-go experiences you have already had with your children. Note others beside the list. What lessons did your children learn?

What lessons did you learn?

Jen is married now, embracing her own adventures with her husband. The kindergarten episode seems so far behind. Natalie, our younger daughter, is in her senior year of college, dreaming big dreams for her future with God. What about your kids? It may be next year or 20 years from now, but your children will grow up and (hopefully) leave home to experience everything God has in store for them. The parent adventure allows you to get them ready for the day of letting go.

Fast-forward to the time when your children will say good-bye to you. Check the qualities you want your adult children to have developed by the time you let them go.

☐ Strong believers in Christ   ☐ Responsible and trustworthy
☐ Spirit of humility   ☐ Serve those in need
☐ Financially independent   ☐ Able to stand up for themselves
☐ Bold in sharing their faith   ☐ Spiritually grounded
☐ Submissive to authority   ☐ Grateful
☐ Positive, optimistic   ☐ Love the Bible
☐ Seek wise counsel   ☐ Servant leaders
☐ Faithfully involved in church ☐ Take initiative, self-motivated
☐ Patriotic   ☐ Independent leaders
☐ Discerning in relationships
☐ Able to distinguish truth from propaganda
☐ Able to admit mistakes and accept responsibility
☐ Other:

As parents whose children have said good-bye, we look back now and see how God taught us to let our children go. It definitely wasn't always easy. I'm sure we occasionally held on too tightly or sometimes didn't push enough; but thankfully, God doesn't demand perfection in letting go. He is patient as we learn, and He understands our challenge.

Jesus Himself understood the challenge. Luke 2:46-50 shows that Joseph and Mary had difficulty letting Jesus grow up to be who His Father wanted Him to be:

Luke 2:46-50, The Message
"The next day [Mary and Joseph] found him in the Temple seated among the teachers, listening to them and asking questions. But his parents were not impressed; they were upset and hurt. His mother said, 'Young man, why have you done this to us? Your father and I have been half out of our minds looking for you.' He said, 'Why were you looking for me? Didn't you know that I had to be here, dealing with the things of my Father?' But they had no idea what he was talking about."

How can you relate to Mary and Joseph's reaction?

Despite Mom and Dad's growing pains, Luke 2:52 tells us that "Jesus increased in wisdom and stature, and in favor with God and with people." In other words, Jesus grew physically, spiritually, and socially.

Why is it important for parents to let go in order for their children to grow—

physically?

spiritually?

socially?

Tim Elmore has identified seven marks indicating that your children are maturing intellectually, emotionally, and spiritually:
1. They are able to keep long-term commitments.
2. They are unshaken by flattery or criticism.
3. They possess a spirit of humility.
4. Their decisions are based on character, not feelings.
5. They consistently express gratitude.
6. They prioritize others before themselves.
7. They seek wisdom before acting.[2]

Place a check mark beside the qualities you already see emerging in your children. Select one and briefly describe an example of the way your children demonstrate this quality.

Letting go helps develop your children for the day when you launch them from your home to begin their own independent adventures with God.

WHOSE KIDS ARE THEY ANYWAY?

It's hard to release something you own. When you think your children belong to you, it's natural to cling to them. You fear every threat and try to protect them from every pain. That's why successfully letting go requires recognizing the owner—the real Father of your kids. He knew them long before you ever thought about becoming a parent. He is the ultimate Provider, Healer, Counselor, and Protector. Reluctant letting go brings anguish, bitterness, and regret. Godly letting go brings freedom, blessing, and adventure! Letting your children go with God early in life allows them to become the kind of adult you want them to be someday.

Colossians 1:16 reminds us that "all things have been created through Him and for Him." *All* means *all*. He made all things, including your child. When you remember that your Maker is also your child's Maker, it changes things. You see yourself as a preparer, getting your kid ready for a life with God and responsible adulthood.

If God is the ultimate owner of our children, what is our role? We are simply, but significantly, their managers, getting them ready for their own adventures with God that they will live out long after we are gone.

When we parent with the end in mind, we realize that our children never really belong to us; they are always God's. We begin to recognize our responsibility to guide them through childhood, phase by phase, change after change, good-bye after good-bye, to a point of independence. Eventually, our children must say good-bye to us to fully embrace God's ultimate plan for their lives. Even in the beginning, God started the family with the parents letting go: "This is why a man leaves his father and mother and bonds with his wife, and they become one flesh" (Gen. 2:24). When you let go from the beginning, it's natural for your kids to leave Mom and Dad, cleaving to their spouses.

We essentially work ourselves out of a parenting job. Our spirit should be like John the Baptist's attitude toward Christ: "He must increase, but I must decrease" (John 3:30). Likewise, our kids' dependence on Christ must increase, and their dependence on us must decrease. This requires that we parents learn to let go.

Check the statement that more accurately describes your parenting.

☐ I think of myself as a steward of my kids. God is their Father.
☐ I think of myself as my children's owner.

In Matthew 25 Jesus told a story that may help us understand our role as stewards of our children and God's role as owner. A master was going on a journey, so he gave responsibility to his servants to manage his talents (possessions) while he was gone. When the owner returned, he asked the servants to report on how they had managed the resources for which they were responsible.

Two of the servants stood before the Master and proudly reported on what they had done with the talents given to them. Each had worked to give back to the Master more than was given to them. They had invested the resources for a good return on the investment. Jesus said to each of them: "Well done, good and faithful slave! You were faithful over a few things; I will put you in charge of many things. Share your master's joy!" (Matt. 25:21,23).

How sad for the servant who received one talent. He had done nothing and risked nothing, trying his best to keep the talent entrusted to him as safe as possible. Jesus said to him: "You evil, lazy slave!" (v. 26).

If you are familiar with the concept of tithing, you are aware that God holds us accountable for the way we spend our money. It all belongs to Him, and we are simply the stewards of what He sends our way. Similarly, we are the stewards of the precious gifts of our children. God has entrusted us with their care, and He will hold us accountable for raising the kids He has lent us. Part of that stewardship involves preparing them for their own adventure with God, separate from Mom and Dad.

> "I had rather you should remain hundreds of miles distant
> from us and have God nigh to you by his Spirit, than to
> have you always with us, and live at a distance from God."[3]
> —*Jonathan Edwards to his daughter, Mary*

God expects believers to manage the truth of who He is in the world. He wants us to invest in the lives of others. What greater joy and what greater responsibility than to multiply our faith through the lives of our children! The Master has given us the responsibility to teach our children about Him. This investment will multiply itself in the lives of many people for generations to come.

The missionary Jim Elliot once said, "He is no fool who gives what he cannot keep to gain that which he cannot lose."[4] When we apply his statement to letting go, it means we cannot keep our kids kids forever. Eventually, they will grow up and move out. So how do we give what we cannot keep? We let go along the way to prepare our children for adulthood. We acknowledge that our role is only one chapter in a life that, Lord willing, will have many more chapters. So we do our part, preparing them and ourselves to release them into adulthood.

When the kids have left our nest, what do they gain that they cannot lose?

Here are just a few examples of what our children gain when we let them go.
- They own their faith in God.
- They are ready to make God known.
- They are ready to use the gifts and abilities God has given them to impact the world.
- They are ready to face life.
- They are ready to make decisions on their own.

What do parents gain by letting their children go?

We parents also gain when we let our kids go. We gain great memories of seeing their progress toward adulthood. We see them growing up and making their own decisions. (Don't be surprised if they vote for a different candidate than you do!) We gain the gratification of knowing that, yes, this went fast, but letting go is right.

Hopefully, parents will gain a thankful heart from their grown-up kids. Your kids may thank you for letting them make some of their own choices on their road to the adult life.

Parents can gain comfort in knowing that their willingness to let go is necessary for their children to fully embrace their faith in God and the plans He has for them. After all, the goal of Christian parenting is to prepare and release kids to embark on their own adventures with God.

Read Jeremiah 29:11. How does knowing that God holds the plans for your children's future affect your approach to parenting?

Jeremiah 29:11

" 'I know the plans I have for you'—this is the Lord's declaration—'plans for your welfare, not for disaster, to give you a future and a hope.' "

BIBLICAL PARENTS WHO LET GO

The Bible provides several examples of parents who recognized that they did not own their kids. While their techniques are … OK, unique by today's standards, these parents clearly acknowledged God as the ultimate Parent of their children.

From fear to freedom (see Ex. 2). As a Hebrew slave, one mother lived in fear for her newborn. After Pharaoh ordered the deaths of all baby boys, she concealed Moses in her house for three months. When she could hide him no longer, she coated a basket with tar and pitch and placed her baby inside. As she set her son adrift on the Nile River, Moses' mom relinquished her role as protector and provider, trusting God to save him. He certainly did.

Back to God (see 1 Sam. 1). In ancient Jewish culture, Hebrew women longed to bear children. After years of praying for a child, Hannah went to the temple and poured out her heart to God with such fervor that the priest thought she was drunk. Hannah promised that if she had a child, she would give him back to God. Eventually, God allowed Hannah to have a son, Samuel. She kept her word and presented him to God at the temple when Samuel was still very young: "I prayed for this boy, and since the Lord gave me what I asked Him for, I now give the boy to the Lord. For as long as he lives, he is given to the Lord" (vv. 27-28).

An obedient mother-in-law (see Ruth 1). Naomi knew what it was like to lose everything. Within a few years her husband and two sons died, leaving her with no immediate family. Instead of desperately clinging to her daughters-in-law, she released them, commanding them to return to their homeland to be blessed with new husbands. One woman left, but Ruth refused. To Naomi's astonishment, Ruth vowed never to leave her mother-in-law. God honored Naomi's decision to let go by giving her Ruth and, eventually, an amazing new son.

Royal results (see 1 Sam. 16). David's father, Jesse, let David go to the fields to care for sheep. That doesn't sound too impressive until you realize that David faced the dangers of lions and bears while protecting and caring for his father's sheep. Although Jesse knew there would be danger, he let David go anyway. That dangerous environment developed David's courage and prepared him to face and defeat Goliath. And defeating Goliath helped prepare him to be the king! God's plan for David was to be the king of Israel, and He used Jesse's willingness to let go to get David ready.

What motivated these parents to let go of their children?

What qualities enabled these parents to let go?

Letting go is an act of love, the greatest foundation for parenting. We let go because it is best for our children, even when it seems not to be best for us. Letting go requires strong faith and trust in God, who loves our children even more than we do and desires for them to take up the purposes He has planned for them.

HOW TO LET GO

How does a parent learn how to let go? Start by letting go today. Review the ideal adult characteristics you identified on page 36. Your children will not transform into independent, godly adults overnight. Letting go starts right now. No matter what their ages are, your children can learn independence. Here are suggestions for letting go at each stage of your children's development.

As you read the following ideas, check the ones you need to implement with your kids.

Infants to six months:
- Pray over them. Have a specific time when you commit to raise each of your children to know God.
- Leave them with others, such as family, friends, and the church nursery. Don't sneak out. This causes anxiety and clingy behavior next time. Instead, say good-bye and reassure them you'll be back. Of course, you need to choose your children's guardian wisely (this is true at every stage).

Mark the continuum to indicate how well you are letting go of your infant.

Holding on too tightly   *Consistently letting go*

"When we leave our child in nursery school for the first time, it won't just be our child's feelings about separation that we will have to cope with, but our own feelings as well—from our present and from our past, parents are extra vulnerable to new tremors from old earthquakes."[5]—*Fred Rogers*

Preschoolers:
- Give them choices. Allow them to start thinking on their own and making decisions. For example: "Apple juice or milk?" "*The Cat in the Hat* or nursery rhymes?" "Sandals or tennis shoes?"
- Let them make mistakes and learn from the consequences. For example, warn your child that she is about to drop something; then let her drop it.

If she is about to spill a glass of milk, tell her; then let it spill. Don't warn her and then fix the problem. Let her clean up her own messes.

- Give age-appropriate responsibilities, such as picking up their toys, getting their blanket, and carrying their bag. They can also help set the table and feed the dog. Don't major on perfection, but value their independence in the completion of the task. Let them do it their way.
- Prepare yourself. Honestly, you're the one who will experience the greatest separation anxiety, not your child. Sometime before preschool, plan a night out—just parents. Leave your child with a trusted baby-sitter.

Mark the continuum to indicate how well you are letting go of your preschooler.

Holding on too tightly   *Consistently letting go*

Elementary age:

- Encourage children to speak to adults. For example, don't let them depend on whispering in your ear when they want you to ask an adult for them. Say, "You can ask them." This will help them interact with others and speak for themselves so that they can function when you're not around.
- Allow them to attend a field trip with you.
- Let them ride the school bus (my kid? Yes, your kid!)
- Have them order their own meal at a restaurant.
- Assign appropriate household responsibilities, such as making their bed, watering plants, and feeding the pet.
- Encourage service responsibilities at church, such as assisting a teacher, cleaning up the church grounds, or serving senior adults.

Mark the continuum to indicate how well you are letting go of your elementary-age child.

Holding on too tightly   *Consistently letting go*

Preadolescence:

- Allow them to sleep over at a friend's house (if you know the parents).
- Provide only necessary assistance with schoolwork. Don't do their projects for them.
- Allow them to disagree with you respectfully and form their own ideas.
- Challenge them to take risks, such as auditioning for the school play or trying out for the team. If they don't make it, pour on the encouragement and teach them again about God's plan for their lives. (See chap. 5, "Pain Happens.")
- Increase their household responsibilities to include preparing a meal, vacuuming, cutting the lawn, or washing the car.
- Encourage serving through the church's preschool program, using their musical abilities, or assisting with the media/sound team. As you identify your child's gifts, interests, and abilitites, work with your church leaders to begin giving your child church experiences in those areas of ministry.

Mark the continuum to indicate how well you are letting go of your preadolescent.

Holding on too tightly   *Consistently letting go*

High schoolers:

- Allow them to get a job and pay for one or two things such as gas, cell phone, and dates or outings with friends.
- Teach basic survival skills such as balancing a checkbook, changing a tire, paying bills, and cutting out coupons.
- Allow them to go on a church mission trip without you.
- Let them plan and coordinate supervised parties at your house like holiday themes and birthdays. Put them in charge of invitations, decorations, and food. Make them work within a budget.
- Encourage them to accept leadership responsibilities in the church through the children's or youth ministry, media ministry, worship team, bookstore, greeting ministry, or grounds maintenance.

Mark the continuum to indicate how well you are letting go of your high schooler.

Holding on too tightly   *Consistently letting go*

College students:

- Help them break away financially. Establish a budget and expect them to work (at least during summer).
- Allow them to make their own dating choices.
- Give freedom over your children's schedules. You don't need to know where they are 24/7.
- Allow college-age children to fight their own battles with professors, friends, and others. Give advice and support, but let them make the final call.
- Allow your children to attend a church of their choosing.
- Let them choose their major, job, and career path. Affirm their gifts, but never quash their dreams.
- Encourage them to assume leadership roles at church by teaching or assisting in the youth ministry; children's or youth camps; or local, national, or international mission trips.

Mark the continuum to indicate how well you are letting go of your college student.

Holding on too tightly   *Consistently letting go*

Part of letting go is teaching responsibility at every age. Your children will mess up, but you don't have to bail them out. When your six-year-old refuses to pick up his toys, don't do it for him. Enforce the consequence (no TV, video games, or soccer practice) until the job is done. Likewise, when your 18-year-old overdraws her checking account for the third time (a real-life story, by the way), insist that she pay the fees and spend time relearning the concept of budgeting.

If you struggle with the idea of letting your children go, spend time in prayer. Acknowledge that your kids belong to God and entrust them to His care. Ask Him to give you wisdom in knowing how to let them go responsibly.

TEACHING SPIRITUAL TRUTH AS YOU GO

Each phase of letting go is an opportunity to live your responsibility and calling as a parent. Every parenting decision you make from birth to young adulthood prepares your children for their own adventures with God.

Deuteronomy 6:5-7

"Love the LORD your God with all your heart, with all your soul, and with all your strength. These words that I am giving you today are to be in your heart. Repeat them to your children. Talk about them when you sit in your house and when you walk along the road, when you lie down and when you get up."

Remember our focal verse for this study? When you love God with all your heart, you can remember that He's in charge, not us. Every time you let go in little and big ways, you emphasize the truth of God and His Word. You remind your children that God holds the plan for their lives. In the ordinary as well as the extraordinary stuff of everyday life, you have the privilege and responsibility of pointing your children to God—the One they will totally depend on when they have left your home.

Speak these truths to your children to get them ready to go with God:

- God created them: "You created my inmost being" (Ps. 139:13, NIV).
- God loves them: nothing "in all creation, will be able to separate us from the love of God" (Rom. 8:39, NIV).
- God has a plan for them: " 'I know the plans I have for you'—this is the LORD's declaration" (Jer. 29:11).
- God has gifted them in unique ways: "You do not lack any spiritual gift" (1 Cor. 1:7).

At every stage of your children's lives, look for ways to let go and teach them the truth of God at the same time.

FROM LIFEWAY RESEARCH

7% Just 7 percent of all parents have a written plan or goal for what they want to accomplish as a parent. Regular churchgoers are particularly likely to have a plan.

The vast majority of parents FEEL FEARFUL when they think about what their kids will face in this world as adults, including one-third who feel this strongly.

Just over half of all parents LOOK FORWARD to the day their kids grow up with excitement that they'll be ready to face the world. Thirty-four percent think of this day with fear and worry over whether they'll be ready, while 15 percent say this is simply too painful to think about.[6]

THE PARENT ADVENTURE PLAN

Review the ideas on pages 43–46 for letting go. What three actions can you take this week to begin letting go?

1.

2.

3.

What can you tell your children about the way God is working in your life as you let them go?

Share Jeremiah 29:11 with your children and assure them that God has a plan for their lives.

PRAYER FOCUS

Father, it is so scary to let go of my children. I want to hold on tightly and protect them from the world. Give me courage to let go so that they will learn to ultimately put their trust in You. Give me wisdom in the day-to-day adventure of parenting to teach my children about You. Help me, Father, to let go a little more today so that they can be ready for all You have planned for them. Most of all, let my children see You in me so that they will come to put their faith in You.

A YES HOME

chapter three

session three GROUP EXPERIENCE

GET TO KNOW YOUR GROUP

DISCUSS what you discovered from your parent adventure after reading chapter 2, "Letting Go."

SHARE an off-the-wall scheme your children have constructed.

WARM-UP

- What signs of creativity do you see in your children?

- What is the craziest request your child has ever made?

WATCH DVD

- Watch DVD session 3.
- What stood out to you in this session?

THE BIBLICAL VIEW

2 Corinthians 1:18-20

"As God is faithful, our message to you is not 'Yes and no.' For the Son of God, Jesus Christ, who was preached among you by us—by me and Silvanus and Timothy— did not become 'Yes and no'; on the contrary, 'Yes' has come about in Him. For every one of God's promises is 'Yes' in Him."

- In what specific ways has God said yes to you personally?

- Turn to the list of Jesus' yeses on pages 57–58. Which one of these yeses means the most to you right now? Why?

- Which of these yeses do your children need to hear right now? Why?

 # THE ADVENTURE

- In your own words describe what a yes home looks like.

- Identify some blessings of a yes home.

- How does a yes home build confidence in your children?

- Did you grow up in a yes home? How does that impact your current home?

- Identify some of the boundaries in your home. How does having a yes home make it easier to say no?

- What is one way you will say yes to your children this week?

- What is one way you will say yes to God this week?

CLOSING THOUGHTS

- Read the following yes responses to God.

    Isaiah 6:8
    Isaiah said yes: "Here I am. Send me."

    Luke 1:38
    Mary said yes: "I am the Lord's slave. May it be done to me according to your word."

    Esther 4:16
    Esther said yes: "I will go to the King, even if it is against the law. If I perish, I perish."

- Create your own yes response to God.

- Ask God to use your home to model His desired relationship with His children.

NEXT WEEK

Next week you will study "Let's Talk." You will learn how sharing life together as a family lays the foundation for your children to talk to God.

A YES HOME

chapter three

2 Corinthians 1:20
"Every one of God's promises is 'Yes' in Him."

The Wilsons' family nights usually went like this: we ate dinner, played a game or two, watched our favorite shows, then hit the sack. Easy enough until our oldest daughter, Jennifer, then six, proposed a wacky idea: why couldn't we eat dinner on the living-room floor?

It was a simple request, clearly something neither Mom nor Dad had ever imagined. We looked at each other, and then Selma responded with two words that began to change our parenting experience: "Why not?"

From that moment family night in the Wilson home was transformed. The weekly spreading of the checkered tablecloth on the living-room floor marked the beginning of family night and family fun.

With Dad's help our living room was magically transformed into exciting destinations. We entered the jungle by moving a few plants around. We constructed campsites (our favorite) by throwing sheets and blankets over furniture. (Caution: These adventures can be messy.) From pizza in the jungle to roasting marshmallows with toothpicks over a candle, family night became the perfect opportunity for our children to be children. In addition to encouraging laughter and imagination, family night allowed Mom and Dad to teach some of life's greatest lessons.

> "Children learn to smile from their parents."[1]
> —*Educator Shinichi Suzuki*

Pizza in the middle of the jungle? Roasting marshmallows on a toothpick over a candle? Why not? Friday nights became a protected tradition in our family for many years. It began with a question sparked by the imagination of a little girl and a mom and a dad who were willing to say yes to her new idea.

Identify a yes moment in your family that became a meaningful experience or tradition. If you can't think of one, start watching for such an opportunity.

BURSTS OF CREATIVITY

Isn't it amazing how God weaves creativity into a child's DNA? Children love to imagine and pretend. They want to touch, explore, test, and challenge the world. Genesis 1:26 tells us that God has made people in His image, which guarantees that within each of us is the amazing potential for creativity. A yes home gives children the freedom to explore their God-given imaginations, with the ultimate goal of discovering who God made them to be.

Genesis 1:26
"God said, 'Let Us make man in Our image, according to Our likeness.' "

If your children are anything like ours, they hatch some pretty imaginative schemes. Have you noticed that children are full of questions? "Daddy, why does a bug crawl?" "Mom, can we touch the stars?" Creating a yes home early on builds an environment for the more challenging questions you want your children to ask as they move through life.

What signs of creativity do you see in your children?

Kids need direction and discipline, for sure. Along with boundaries, however, children crave a place to exercise physically, intellectually, emotionally, and spiritually. A yes home with clearly established boundaries gives them room to stretch, run, and grow—under your guidance and instruction. As parents, we have the responsibility to provide an environment in which we can nurture the gifts, talents, and abilities God has placed in our children. We call this a yes home.

Define a yes home in your own words.

Being open to ideas from your children, going on their kind of vacation, solving problems their way, eating family-night dinners where they want to eat them—experiences like these create a yes home. Saying yes to your children, when you can, builds a healthy environment in your home. It sets the tone for healthy relationships founded on respect and value for each family member.

There are hundreds of ways to build a yes home, even when your children are young. It can begin with the simple, everyday events of life. For example, a three-year-old wants to play with plastic blocks in the bathtub. Mom thinks to herself, *The blocks have always been in the bedroom. I've never thought about using them in the tub. But why not? I'm not going to say no when I can say yes.* So she says to her child, "Yes, let's give them a bath first. Then they can join you in the tub." That same kid, at 15, may ask whether the sleepover can be at your house. Once again, if there are no major problems and she agrees to her part in getting ready, then why not?

"What a child doesn't receive he can
seldom later give."[2] —*P. D. James*

Our friends, parents of three, started a yes home in the kitchen with weekly special dinners. It started when one of their kids asked, "Why can't we make dinner some-times to help Mom?" For years afterward, one night each week, a different family member would prepare dinner. The younger ones had Mom's oversight, of course.

Saying yes to a child's cooking creation was understandably challenging. No doubt eating some of those creations was challenging too! However, each week everyone celebrated the contribution to the family dinner. The child's creativity, set free by the parents' yes, developed a new weekly ritual that lasted for years.

Would you say your home is currently a yes home?　☐ **Yes**　☐ **No**

If not, why do you think your parenting style tends toward saying no?

BIBLICAL MODELS OF YES

God's Word provides a framework for parents to create a yes home. We serve a yes God who longs to teach us through His Word. When we read the Bible, we can recognize God's parameters for our children's behavior and His guidelines for their healthy development. Then we can align our yeses with God's yeses in order to spiritually impact our family. Christian parents should filter every yes in their homes through the principles of God's Word.

Read 2 Corinthians 1:18-20 below. How have God's promises been made available to every believer?

2 Corinthians 1:18-20

"As God is faithful, our message to you is not 'Yes and no.' For the Son of God, Jesus Christ, who was preached among you us—Silvanus, Timothy— did not become 'Yes and no'; on the contrary, 'Yes' has come about in Him. For every one of God's promises is 'Yes' in Him. Therefore the 'Amen' is also through Him for God's glory through us.' "

Ultimately, a yes home is important because you want your child to know the God of yes! God said yes to us when He gave His only Son to die for us so that we can live a yes relationship with Him. Through Jesus Christ we can live a yes life. Here are some of the yeses He speaks into our lives:

- Yes, you can ask Me for wisdom (see Jas. 1:5).
- Yes, I will never stop loving you (see Rom. 8:37-38).
- Yes, you can do all things through Me (see Phil. 4:13).
- Yes, I will finish what I started in you (see Phil. 1:6; 1 Thess. 5:24).
- Yes, I will forgive you (see Eph. 1:7; 1 John 1:9).
- Yes, you can have a full and meaningful life (see John 10:10).
- Yes, I will protect you (see Ps. 32:7; 18:10).
- Yes, you can approach Me with confidence (see Jas. 5:16; 1 John 5:14-15).
- Yes, I have a plan for you (see Jer. 29:11).
- Yes, I can work everything in your life for good (see Rom. 8:28).
- Yes, you will spend eternity in heaven with Me (see John 14:1-4).

- Yes, you are beyond condemnation (see Rom. 8:1).
- Yes, you are a member of My kingdom (see Col. 1:13).
- Yes, you have been adopted (see Rom. 8:15).
- Yes, you have access to God at any moment (see Eph. 2:18).
- Yes, you will never be abandoned (see Heb. 13:5).
- Yes, you have an imperishable inheritance (see 1 Pet. 1:4).

Go back and check truths that your children particularly need to hear now. If you have more than one child, write the appropriate child's name beside each promise you have checked. Start praying about opportunities to share these yeses with your children.

What incredible promises! And there are so many more yes truths in God's Word! Building a yes home prepares your children to say yes to God. In every yes experience you have as a family, teach your children a yes truth about God.

Many examples in Scripture show us what it means to say yes to God.

Mary said yes. " 'I am the Lord's slave,' said Mary. 'May it be done to me according to your word' " (Luke 1:38). Mary's yes gave her the privilege of giving birth to God's Son.

Esther said yes. "I will go to the king, even if it is against the law. If I perish, I perish" (Esth. 4:16). Esther's yes modeled bravery and amazing faith in God in a difficult situation.

Paul said yes. "Immediately, he began proclaiming Jesus in the synagogues: 'He is the Son of God' " (Acts 9:20). Paul's yes to God meant the start of many early churches throughout the known world.

David said yes. "David said, "The LORD who rescued me from the paw of the lion and the paw of the bear will rescue me from the hand of the Philistine" (1 Sam. 17:37). David's yes displayed faith in God that would be vital throughout his reign as the king of Israel.

Abraham said yes. "Abram went, as the LORD had told him. ... Abram was 75 years old when he left Haran" (Gen. 12:4). Abram's responsive yes at 75 became the door through which God established His chosen people.

What have you learned from these men and women who said yes to God?

Notice that a risk was required for each biblical character to say yes to God and that each responded with faith and obedience. Saying yes to God usually involves risk. It means rejecting the status quo and obeying God even when it costs something. That's the real adventure. A yes home creates an environment that points your children to God and gets them ready to say yes to Him.

THE BLESSINGS OF SAYING YES

God has planted gifts in your children. You have the privilege of igniting those gifts through a yes home environment. By saying yes to your children when you can, you value their creativity, raise their confidence, and encourage them to explore the passions God has placed in them to carry out the plans He has for their lives. Often this means coloring outside the box.

Check the statement that describes your willingness to let your children color outside the box.

☐ I am more likely to emphasize rules over creativity.
☐ I freely allow my children to express their creativity.
☐ I sometimes encourage my children's creativity, but
    I recognize that I should probably say yes more often.

Fast-forward a few years. How can a yes environment impact your grown-up child? Maybe he will continue thinking outside the box in other areas of his life. Perhaps he will find a cure for a disease or develop new systems in education, in business, in technology, or on the mission field. Maybe she will have the courage to step out on faith and say yes to God's call on her life. A yes attitude could help your children fight comfort, complacency, materialism, and mediocrity, pursuing God and His plans throughout their lives.

A yes home can develop your child spiritually, emotionally, and physically in the following ways.

A yes home empowers. The three-year-old who gets to put her toys in the bathtub because she thought of it has been encouraged to think outside the (toy) box. Her confidence in her own creativity will grow. Over the years this confidence will begin to release the abilities and passions God has placed in your child. When she is ready to embrace Christ and own her faith, she will be ready to unleash these gifts to impact the world with the truth of Jesus Christ.

Identify one way your home environment empowers your children to express their abilities and interests.

A yes home builds self-esteem. Children feel valued and respected when Mom and Dad take time to listen to them. In a yes home their voice is not only heard but also expected! The yes mind-set says to the child, "We want your input. Your ideas are important to us. Part of your role is to share your suggestions, your opinions, and your viewpoint with your family. When we can, we are going to say yes to your idea. But regardless, your voice is needed and welcome." This message will build confidence and courage in your children so that in the future they will have the confidence to speak up about critical issues of faith and justice.

Identify one way your home environment builds your children's self-esteem.

"When I think of my father, the memories that bubble
   to the surface are not policy or politics. They are
   of the man who opened a child's imagination."[3]
—*Patti Davis, daughter of Ronald Reagan*

A yes home encourages. From ages 6 to 16, children's confidence will skyrocket when parents confer value on them by considering and accepting their ideas. Yeses encourage them to explore their gifts and passions. With each yes you are ultimately getting them ready to say yes to God, to His ways, and to His plans for their lives. Each yes is also an opportunity for you to encourage them with God's truth about the situation.

Identify one way your home environment encourages your children to explore their gifts and to know God.

My mom was dying of cancer. Her hair was gone because of her chemo treatments, she was hooked to an oxygen tank, and her body was weak. But her mind was sharp. As she sat on our living-room couch, our girls, seven and nine, were playing around the house. I had finished a load of laundry and was sitting with her, folding the clothes. Mom spoke some powerful words to me that day, words of affirmation but also words of challenge: "Selma, always remember that your girls are more important than so much of life—more important than a clean house, perfect meals, and even those clean clothes. Spend more time with them playing, reading, and just being. You and Rodney are good parents, but don't ever lose sight of the important things in life."

I received many gifts and blessings from my godly mom and dad, but that day is marked forever in my memory. In Mom's own way she was saying, "Build a yes home." As her days on this earth were coming to a close, she could more clearly see the connection between this life and eternity. The wisdom of saying no to the less important things in life and saying yes to the critical role of being a mom hit me full force. In my own noble quest to have a perfect house, be a perfect hostess, and be a perfect minister's wife, I was saying yes to many things; but that was causing me to say no to something more important—my children. Looking into eternity can give us perspective! Making sure my children knew God was more important than anything else.

Is God currently asking you to say yes to something that would help teach your children about God? What is holding you back?

LEARNING TO SAY YES

When your child asks you whether he can do something off-the-wall, the default response is no. No is safe. No is status quo. And no is a lot easier to say. There's no risk involved. No messes to clean up. No wondering what others would think if they knew the whole family played outside in the rain one day.

On the other hand, the yes response has to be intentional; and it starts before the question ever comes. Parents need to predetermine that they will at least consider their kids' ideas and not immediately write them off as immature. To change your default setting, turn off the instant no and ponder your child's request. Even when the answer needs to be no, your child can feel valued that you respectfully considered her idea.

Here are some yes questions your kids may ask you.

- **Preschooler:** "Mom, may I play dress-up with some of your old clothes?" "Dad, will you teach me how to dig up worms?"
- **Elementary age:** "May we get up in the middle of the night and watch for meteors?"
- **Preadolescent:** "May I invite my friends over for a campout?"
- **High schooler:** "May I go on the student mission trip to Brazil?"
- **College student:** "May I study abroad?"

List some things your kids have recently asked to do.

Check any you said yes to. Draw a star beside those you wish you had said yes to.

THE BOUNDARIES OF YES

Even in a yes home it is sometimes necessary to say no. Along with hundreds of yeses, parents also need to clearly define the nos. Children want and need boundaries. Boundaries create an environment of security and confidence. Your children want to know you love them enough to say no.

> "Without discipline and respect in the home, there
> is none in the world."—*A parent from Texas*

Our Heavenly Father perfectly understands our need for boundaries. He gave us Ten Commandments in the context of hundreds of yes-driven promises (see Ex. 20:1-16). He gave Adam one no tree in the garden in addition to numerous yes trees. Both the promises and the boundaries were crystal clear: "You are free to eat from any tree of the garden, but you must not eat from the tree of knowledge of good and evil, for on the day you eat from it, you will certainly die" (Gen. 2:16-17).

Just like Adam and Eve, we have a sin nature. Even in the middle of all the yeses God gives us, we choose to disobey God and do the one thing He clearly tells us not to do. Whatever the age of your children, you will see the same tendency in them. "Son, you can play anywhere on the playground, but don't go beyond the slide." Where does the child immediately want to go? Beyond the slide!

What boundaries do your children tend to rebel against most?

Respect was an absolute yes in our home. From our earliest years of parenting to the launching of the girls, we insisted that family members show respect to one another in word and deed, creating a no-tolerance mind-set toward disrespect. Disagreement and even anger were permitted but only within the boundaries of respect at all times. Disrespect was firmly and immediately corrected, always in the context of teaching our girls about God and His Word.

Other nonnegotiables in the Wilson family:

- No, you do not get a pass on helping around the house. Every member of the family has daily responsibilities.
- No, you can't play at your friend's house unless I meet the parents.
- No, you can't stay up late and sleep through church on Sunday.

What are some of the most important boundaries you have established in your home?

If you have not established the consequences for violating these boundaries, decide on them now and write them below. Then plan a time to communicate the boundaries and the consequences to your kids.

Just like yeses, your nos aren't randomly applied in a "Because I said so" style. Ephesians 6:4 tells dads not to exasperate their kids. Parents are not to act like tyrants or dictators. Rather, be respectful of your child even when you need to be firm. Sometimes trying to find that balance kept us on our knees.

Ephesians 6:4

"Fathers, don't stir up anger in your children, but bring them up in the training and instruction of the Lord."

When you say no to your child, make it a teachable time (it may require a cooling-off period first). Both your yeses and your nos prepare your children for life with God. He offers hundreds of yes promises you can daily point out to your children. When they need to hear no, you can explain why the no exists and why God loves us enough to make certain things off limits. As your kids learn to respect your nos in a predominantly yes home, they can grow to honor God's nos in His yes-filled Word.

Underline the no in each of the following verses.

Proverbs 6:6

"Go to the ant, you slacker! Observe its ways and become wise."

Proverbs 12:19

"Truthful lips endure forever, but a lying tongue, only a moment."

Matthew 6:25

"Don't worry about your life, what you will eat or what you will drink; or about your body, what you will wear."

1 Corinthians 10:14

"Flee from idolatry."

Ephesians 5:18

"Don't get drunk with wine, which leads to reckless actions, but be filled with the Spirit."

Ephesians 6:1

"Children, obey your parents in the Lord, because this is right."

1 Thessalonians 4:7

"God has not called us to impurity, but to sanctification."

Seeking God's guidance in parenting will help you know when to say yes and when to say no. We encourage you to save your nos for the most important issues in life and to say yes when you can.

You will find that in the proper context of a yes home, the nos can actually become easier. As a 16-year-old novice driver, I was getting ready for a big date when a storm arrived with ice and sleet. My dad entered my room with a rare no on his mind. I will never forget that talk. I've drawn from it many times in my own parenting. He told me he trusted my driving, but he didn't trust others in the icy weather.

Then Dad played the trump card. He said, "Son, you know I don't tell you no very often, but tonight … no." He had me. Yes, I was disappointed; but the way he said no, along with the fact that he rarely told me no, gave me no ammunition to disagree with his decision. Even in the context of this particular no, this was a yes home in action. All of Dad's and Mom's previous yeses impacted my acceptance of this rare no.

Mark the scale to rate the way you are establishing and communicating boundaries in your home.

	Low	High
I have established clearly defined boundaries for my children.		1 2 3 4 5
I clearly communicate boundaries to my children.		1 2 3 4 5
My nos are based on biblical principles.		1 2 3 4 5
I use nos to teach my children about life with God.		1 2 3 4 5
I pray and read God's Word to gain wisdom for saying yes or no to my children.		1 2 3 4 5
I say no in the context of a yes home.		1 2 3 4 5

TEACHING SPIRITUAL TRUTH AS YOU GO

Each yes and each no in our parent adventure gives us an opportunity to teach our children about God and His work in the world and in our lives. Recall the foundational verses for our parent adventure:

Deuteronomy 6:5-7
"Love the LORD your God with all your heart, with all your soul, and with all your strength. These words that I am giving you today are to be in your heart. Repeat them to your children. Talk about them when you sit in your house and when you walk along the road, when you lie down and when you get up."

Here is an example of the way you could use a yes to teach your children about God. You have just moved to a new community in mid-December; and your 10-year-old, who loves to sing, asks whether the family can go Christmas caroling to the homes on your new street.

How could you say yes in a way that would teach your child about God?

This scenario might require a family conference, but one outcome could be "You know, Ryan, you have the ability to sing; and the Bible tells us we need to use our gifts for the Lord. Caroling could be a way you can use your gift. If you will start each song, we'll carol with you."

Here is an example of the way you could teach your children about God as you say no. Your 12-year-old tells you that "everyone" is going to a middle-school party at the Findley home Friday night and that her social acceptance depends on her going. Parties at the Findley home are well known. You do not approve of the activities allowed and what appears to be a lack of parental supervision.

How could you say no in a way that would teach your child about God?

No family conference needed here, just firm parental leadership. But rather than exasperating your daughter, speak the truth in love (see Eph. 4:15). Your response could be something like "God tells me in His Word that I am responsible for helping you see what is right and wrong at this point in your life. You will decide that on your own one day, but this is my call for now. I cannot allow you to go because of the activities that are permitted. I am open to discussing other options for social activities with your peers, including having a social event at our home. Why don't we brainstorm what we can do and use this Friday night as a special family outing? Or if you want to have a friend over to spend the night, that would be fine."

Throughout each phase of parenting, you will have many opportunities to say yes and many opportunities to say no. Remember that each yes and each no prepares your child for life with God. Ask God to give you wisdom to know when to say yes and when to say no.

A WARNING FOR YES HOMES

Parents, we must warn you: yes homes are kid-magnets! If you begin to build a yes home, not only will you impact your children; but you will also draw other kids from your church, school, neighborhood, and community. People want to be in a yes home. As each member of your family learns to say yes to God's work in his or her life, those who walk through your door, sit at your table, come to your cookout, and sleep over in living-room tents will also experience it!

Your child's friends will want to come to your house to hang out. Your house will get even messier, and you might be inconvenienced; but you'll have limitless opportunities to teach many children the truth of God. We vividly remember the little-girl sleepovers and the overnight teenage parties. Many, many children and teenagers passed through the doors of our home. Food was always involved, as well as lots of laughter, music, games, and frequent opportunities to share the truth of God and His plans for life.

Get ready. God wants to use your family and your yes home to impact the world for Him!

How have you been able to encourage your children's friends to say yes to God?

FROM LIFEWAY RESEARCH

Most parents describe their HOME ENVIRONMENT as positive. A majority say their home is—

74%
- supportive (74 percent);
- positive (71 percent);
- encouraging (69 percent);
- active (69 percent);
- joyful (57 percent);
- relaxed (51 percent);
- optimistic (50 percent).[4]

THE PARENT ADVENTURE PLAN

Look back over this chapter and identify three things you can do this week to build a yes home.

1.

2.

3.

What can you tell your child about ways you have said yes or no to God in your life?

Yes:

No:

How can you communicate God's yeses and nos to your child? Select at least one Scripture verse to share with them this week. Look through this chapter for some ideas.

PRAYER FOCUS

"Father, thank You for the blessing of being a parent. Give me faith and courage to say yes to You in my own life. Help me build a yes home so that my children will learn more about who You are and will be ready to say yes to You. Give me wisdom and courage to be strong with my nos and to know where to set boundaries for my children. Thank You for saying no to me and for giving me boundaries to live by. Thank You for the yeses You speak to me every day. Help my children see You in me."

LET'S TALK

chapter four

session four GROUP EXPERIENCE

GET TO KNOW YOUR GROUP

DISCUSS what you discovered from your parent adventure after reading chapter 3, "A Yes Home."

NAME different ways of communicating, for example, e-mail and text messaging.

DISCUSS how different communication vehicles affect conversation. Communicating is more than transmitting words. It includes environment, facial expression, body language, trust level, and so forth. Give examples of how your children communicate in ways other than words.

WARM-UP

Describe the strangest place you and your child ever had a serious conversation. What started the exchange?

WATCH DVD

- Watch DVD session 4.
- What stood out to you in this session?

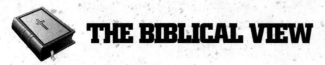 **THE BIBLICAL VIEW**

Proverbs 18:21
"Life and death are in the power of the tongue."

- How is this true in parenting?

Psalm 78:1,2-4,7
"My people, hear my instruction;
listen to what I say.
I will speak mysteries from the past—
things we have known
and that our fathers have passed down to us.
"We must not hide them from their children,
but must tell a future generation
the praises of the LORD,
His might, and the wonderful works
He has performed.
so that they might put their confidence in God
and not forget God's works, but keep His commandments."

- Why is it your responsibility as a parent to communicate God's truth to your children?

Exodus 12:26-27

"When your children ask you, 'What does this ceremony mean to you?' then tell them, 'It is the Passover sacrifice to the LORD, who passed over the houses of the Israelites in Egypt and spared our homes when he struck down the Egyptians.' Then the people bowed down and worshiped."

- How can you live a life that prompt spiritual questions from your children?

 **THE ADVENTURE**

- Why is communication essential for influencing your children?

- How can you have tough talks with your children but still keep your relationship strong?

- Identify some of the forums for talking with your children on pages 77–81. How can you better use these opportunities to develop relationships with your children and encourage them to talk?

- How does small talk build the trust needed to reach deeper levels of communication?

- If every conversation you have with your kids affects the next one, how will you make the most of the conversations awaiting you this week?

- As a child, what kind of communication did you experience with your parents?

- Review the levels of communication on pages 89–93. Identify the areas in which your family needs to improve.

CLOSING THOUGHTS

- How can you talk to your children about God this week?

- Ask God to provide opportunities to go beyond small talk with your children.

- Ask God to make you aware of moments when you can impact your children through your words.

NEXT WEEK

Next week "Pain Happens" will help you teach your children about the reality of pain and how to recognize God working through the tough times of life.

LET'S TALK

chapter four

Proverbs 18:21
"Life and death are in the power of the tongue."

"I think you love Jennifer more than me." Natalie, age four, had called a family conference. We were all gathered in the living room when she boldly made this statement.

We had begun having family conferences in our home when the girls were
in preschool. The rules were simple: anyone could call a family conference for any
reason. We held family conferences about vacations, sharing household chores,
getting a pet, negotiating allowance, mission projects, Christmas plans, critical
family decisions, and many other topics. It became an informal way every member
of our family could express their views, learn to listen, and help one another. The
family conference also became a key family forum for prayer as we took the ordinary
stuff of life to an extraordinary God for guidance and help.

We can't remember everything that was said at this particular conference,
but this time together allowed Natalie to express herself openly. We laugh about
it now, but we were able to deal with something that could have become a critical
issue. What if Natalie had been unable to express her view? We are glad we had
a safe place for her to share her feelings.

What are some issues your family has recently talked about?

What are some issues your family needs to talk about?

TIME TO TALK

Talking is essential in the parent adventure. As we learned in chapter 1, God's Word is very clear that it is the parents' responsibility to pass the baton of faith to their children. Intentionally interrupting our busy lives to engage in meaningful conversations with our kids is key to teaching them how to live a life that pleases God and how to see things from His perspective. We always need to be on the lookout for teachable moments in our children's lives.

Read Exodus 12:26-27. What normal life event would prompt this teachable moment for parents?

Exodus 12:26-27

"When your children ask you, 'What does this ritual mean to you?' you are to reply, 'It is the Passover sacrifice to the LORD, for He passed over the houses of the Israelites in Egypt when He struck the Egyptians and spared our homes.' "

As Hebrew parents observed Passover, their children would have questions about its meaning, creating an opportunity for their parents to teach them about their faith. This passage has clear implications for Christian parents today.

- We need to live a godly lifestyle that will prompt questions from our children about the way we live and practice our faith.
- We need to anticipate these questions and be prepared to answer our children, not with a sermon but with a well-thought-out response that will make sense to them—an answer on their level. When your children ask about spiritual matters, be ready!

What are your children seeing in your life that would cause them to ask questions about God?

Psalm 78 gives us a clear picture of parents' responsibility to talk to our children about God.

Psalm 78:1-4,5-7
"My people, hear my instruction;
listen to what I say.
I will declare wise sayings;
I will speak mysteries from the past—
things we have heard and known
and that our fathers have passed down to us.
We must not hide them from their children,
but must tell a future generation
the praises of the LORD,
His might, and the wonderful works
He has performed.
He commanded our fathers
to teach their children
so that a future generation—
children yet to be born—might know.
They were to rise and tell their children
so that they might put their confidence in God
and not forget God's works,
but keep His commandments."

What does this Scripture say you should talk to your kids about?

According to the psalm, what are the reasons for talking to your children?

On the next page look again at our key verse for *The Parent Adventure*. Underline the words that relate to communicating with your children.

Deuteronomy 6:5-7

"Love the LORD your God with all your heart, with all your soul, and with all your strength. These words that I am giving you today are to be in your heart. Repeat them to your children. Talk about them when you sit in your house and when you walk along the road, when you lie down and when you set up."

Talking to our kids is required if we are going to obey God's command to teach them the ways of God. This chapter will help you build strong communication between you and your children, all for the purpose of connecting them to God.

SETTING THE STAGE TO TALK

The right environment is critical for communication. The busyness of 21st-century family life may be the greatest challenge to talking with your child. We are not going to ask you to check out of the culture and get rid of your 24/7 technology toys, but we are going to identify some steps you can take to talk with your kids in the middle of doing life. These ideas will help you create an environment that prompts conversations. Although the subjects will change, each conversation will be an opportunity for you to teach your child about God. For more on the issue of busyness, see *Freedom from Busyness* by Michael Zigarelli.

> "The best inheritance a person can give to his
> children is a few minutes of his time each day."[1]
> —O. A. Battista

No matter where you and your children are on the journey of life, you can practice these ideas. Most of these steps will take minutes, not hours or days; but they will begin to build relationships between you and your children that will last a lifetime, relationships that will allow you to teach them about God.

Family conferences. Anyone in the family can call a conference anytime for any reason, and everyone in the family is part of the time together. Keep it informal, but make it a total family experience. No topic is off limits. Start early and build this practice into your home. Safe topics will allow for more serious talks that will happen in time.

Does your family have family conferences? ☐ Yes ☐ No

If not, how would they aid communication in your family?

Bedtime. Pay close attention to the minutes before your children go to sleep. At the end of a day defenses are down, and your kids may be more willing to share their thoughts. Turn off the noise of life—computers, iPods, DVDs, cell phones, and TV (a lot to unplug!) and spend a few minutes together as a family. It can be a time of laughter and fun as everyone gets ready for bed (when our girls were little, they rode "Daddy horsy" off to bed). Predictability and routine build confidence and trust, creating intimate levels of talk. This is also a great time for prayer. You are more likely to share from your heart at night. What an opportunity for you to teach God's truths and the power of talking with Him! Bedtime is therefore an ideal opportunity to pray and read God's Word together as a family.

Bedtime is also a great time for the family to read together. Books are great adventures for all members of the family. Rodney spent years of daddy-daughter times reading books to the girls. We went through *The Chronicles of Narnia* and many other great works of literature. Books can also spark great life discussions.

What bedtime rituals does your family have?

How could you use bedtime more effectively to engage in genuine communication?

Mornings. Like your family, we have some members who love mornings and others who would prefer to skip them entirely. Rodney and Natalie wake up ready to talk, sing, and happily greet the world. Selma and Jen would usually like joyful morning people to keep their distance.

Who are the morning people in your household?

Who in your family would rather skip mornings?

Work on mornings. They set the tone for the rest of the day for every member of the family. Minutes count in families and in life. Don't lose valuable time together by allowing the day to begin on a sour note. We highly recommend that you start by getting up a few minutes before everyone else in the family and spending quiet time with God. Even a few minutes of focused time will make a difference as the chaos of the day starts full speed ahead!

Be intentional and creative about specific things each family member can do to make the mornings more positive. You may need to get clothes and school supplies ready the night before. Think about giving the slow-to-rise child 15 extra minutes to get his motor going. Maybe you can have a time of prayer in which you focus everyone on God's goodness and provision for the day. Focus hard on your communication with your children in the last five minutes before you separate for the day. Make sure your child starts the day with a blessing from you.

Underline some ideas in the previous paragraphs that you would like to implement to improve communication in the mornings. Add other ideas below that you have thought of.

Reentry. If any member of the family has been apart during the day, emphasize the back-together moments. Stop, focus, touch, make eye contact, say that you missed them, and share together the stories of the day.

When I was a young girl, one of my most powerful memories was the reentry time with my mom after school each day. When I got off the school bus, my mom was waiting for me. She usually had a snack waiting, and we sat in the kitchen and talked. She wanted to know about my day. Sometimes it would be just a few minutes, but sometimes I would have a lot to say. These times built a strong bond of security for me.

What reentry practices do you use with your children?

Mealtime. LifeWay research indicates that only 57 percent of families say they regularly eat together as a family.[2] A great deal of research has been done on the impact of family meals together and their value to children. The benefits include increased nutritional value, high performance in school, a high degree of belonging, and fewer behavioral problems. One of the greatest values of mealtimes together, however, is the focused time for families to talk and share life together. Let mealtime be a focused time to invest in your children.

Does your family have most meals together?   ☐ Yes   ☐ No

If so, are they providing valuable opportunities to talk with your children?   ☐ Yes   ☐ No

"Perhaps no other activity provides intimate sharing and conversation time like a calm, comfortable meal together. The rush of today's schedules prevents families from having this provision."
—*A parent from Mississippi*

Maybe it's impossible for your family to have every meal together, but call a family conference and agree on how many meals you can share. Take turns preparing the food. Meal preparation is a great life-teaching experience. Vary where and how you have the meal (a picnic in the backyard, a formal meal with good china and candles, a blanket on the living-room floor). Eating together as a family creates opportunities to talk to your children about God and to discover how He is working in their lives.

Family adventures. From living-room picnics and backyard campouts to weeklong vacations together, every family adventure is an opportunity to share life together and talk, preparing your children for life with God.

Identify the latest adventure your family has had together.

Check the focused times you think you are using well to communicate with your family.

☐ Family conferences ☐ Bedtime ☐ Mornings
☐ Reentry ☐ Mealtime ☐ Family adventures

Circle one area in which you would like to improve. Describe how you can use that time with your family to intentionally set the stage for healthy communication.

A pattern of good communication lays a foundation for addressing the weightier issues of life that inevitably come. Perry McGuire, an attorney in Douglasville, Georgia, and his wife, Lauren, have four children. Perry has described the way he set the stage for an important discussion with his son—"the talk" about sex. After reading several books and listening to tapes, Perry took his son, Reed, to the beach for a father-son weekend.

We took long walks that weekend. I'd ask Reed what he understood about the things discussed on the tapes. I'd have him explain them to me. And I'm glad I did. Sometimes it was clear that Reed was clueless, and it's this sort of cluelessness that could get him in trouble in the world.

Of course, these walks resulted in other things. It was tough not to spontaneously explode into gut-busting laughter at some of the things Reed would say. I pictured us in a serious clinical setting, probably much like psychologists must be with their clients. I was serious and let him know that every question is a good question. When he gave an incorrect interpretation, I let him know that I could understand how he made his conclusion; then I'd give him the correct explanation.

The second result was my new-found ability to lecture to the sea. Sometimes I simply could not look at Reed, and I realized he had the same problem because he'd be looking down at the sand. But I was determined to tell him all the things I wish I had known, so I toughed it out (wiping the perspiration from my forehead as needed).

We also had some great rec time, an important component in creating a positive experience for both of us. Of course, the beach in January is not the most happening place, but we did get in a couple rounds of miniature golf and watched a couple of guy movies.

In the end, what hit me like a rock was that inside this big boy (and I do mean big—Reed is almost as tall and as strong as I am) is still a boy—naive, curious, and a little scared of what his future holds. The greatest gift I can give him is knowledge of the truth and security in knowing that he will not have to go it alone. His Heavenly Father and his earthly father will stand shoulder to shoulder with him. And it will be his dad, not his friends or the media, who has his back.[3]

What actions did this father take to prepare to talk with his son?

Focused times with your kids help you build talk systems into your family. Talk systems are focused times you build into your family to share, listen, and learn from one another. Before you earn the right to talk to your kids about the big stuff—such as relationships, spiritual growth, and sex—show that you are interested in talking about the seemingly trivial things—clothes, sports, who sits beside whom at lunch. From bugs to boys, from kiddie pools to the swim team, from playing dress-up to a formal social function, from fingerpainting to modern art, a healthy talk system can allow you to connect your kids' passions, abilities, and interests to God and the plans He has for their lives.

What passions, abilities, and interests are you seeing in your children as you talk with them?

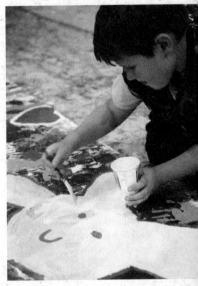

How can you use these discussions to connect your kids to God's plan for their lives?

Showing interest in your children's world at every stage of their childhood creates an environment for you to connect them to God and to the great adventure He has planned just for them.

CAN YOU HEAR ME NOW?

What would you say if we asked you to name a parent's most vital communication tool? As you teach your children and prepare them for life with God, it is critical that you talk but even more critical that you listen—with your eyes as well as your ears.

We love to teach and counsel. One reason is because of the immediate feedback we get on what we've just shared. If we take a moment to notice, it becomes evident whether our point was clear. As that brilliant philosopher Yogi Berra would say, "You can observe a lot by just watching."[4]

For example, when counseling couples, we can tell within the first few minutes whether the husband feels respected and the wife feels loved, not by the words they say but by the nonverbal cues they give each other. Respect for men and love for wives are key indicators of the health of their marriage.

The same is true in parenting. Once you've shared a thought, spoken a word of wisdom, answered a question, or explained why the level of discipline was given, then watch. Most kids will immediately let you know if you're making sense. But you've got to watch and listen for nonverbal clues.

Kids often scream nonverbal messages through facial expressions, body language, eye contact, and voice tone. In order for parents to really hear their children, they must put all the communication pieces together, both the nonverbals and the words being said.

What nonverbal communication have you noticed in your children?

☐ Facial expressions   ☐ Body language
☐ Eye contact   ☐ Voice tone
☐ Other:

Check the way you respond to nonverbal signals from your kids.

☐ I am sensitive to these signals, try to interpret what they mean, and respond accordingly.
☐ I haven't really noticed nonverbals.
☐ I have noticed nonverbals, but I ignore them and focus only on the words.
☐ Other:

Some parents tend to talk *to* their kids and not *with* them, oblivious to nonverbal signals, resulting in a fruitless one-way conversation. Stop the lecture long enough to see whether you have a listening audience or just a body in front of you. There's a big difference. If it seems that you're talking to a brick wall, stop, rephrase, ask questions, and try to get your child to respond.

If your children are not openly sharing through words, pay even closer attention to what they are saying through nonverbal cues. You may need to initiate the talk by saying things like:

- "Son, you seem sad."
- "I can tell you're really angry."
- "I notice how happy you are when you …"

When our girls were preschoolers, we started a family saying: "Look at my nose." Who would have thought healthy parent-child communication would involve a nasal exam? But it was a fun, light way to get their attention. Some parents might say, "Look at my eyes." Parents often use this technique to emphasize discipline and correction. We also used our children's undivided attention to bless them and teach them truths about God:

- "Jennifer, we are so glad God let us be your parents."
- "Natalie, God has a plan for your life."
- "Jennifer, God has given you some amazing gifts and abilities."
- "Natalie, we are proud of you for just being you."

What are some "Look at my nose" statements you can make to your children that would affirm them and point them to God?

Here are 10 power statements you can make with your kids.

- "Yes."
- "How can I pray for you?"
- "Will you forgive me?"
- "God has a plan for you!"
- "We are excited that you are growing up [entering a new stage of life]!"
- "I know it hurts."
- "You are more important to me than [report cards, work, sports, etc.]."
- "I'm so glad you are in our family."
- "I love you too much to let you do that."
- "Try to be patient with me. I've never been the parent of a ___-year-old before." (Caution: This works only with the firstborn!)

"The quickest way for a parent to get a child's attention is to sit down and look comfortable."[5]—*Lane Olinghouse*

The "Look at my nose" technique goes two ways. You want your child to zero in when you make an important point. Likewise, you need to give her your undivided attention when she is expressing herself. Carefully watch your children to see if your words get through. Do they hear and receive your encouragement? Do they seem confused? Do they seem to be holding back something they need to say?

What do your children do when they want your attention?

Some nonverbal expressions threaten communication. Be especially alert to these signals:

- Rolling eyes: I'm annoyed, and I disagree with you.
- Crossed arms: I'm closed and upset.
- Tapping/fidgeting: I'm nervous and tense.
- One-word response: I feel my thoughts don't matter, or I'm too upset to talk.

Go back and check the reactions you have seen in your children. How do you typically react?

When your child responds in these ways, you face a greater challenge in drawing out productive communication. Use the method suggested earlier: stop, rephrase, ask questions, and try to get your child to respond. If these steps don't work, you may need to take time to cool off and meet later to talk again. At the same time, check your own nonverbals. Uncross your arms and don't hover over your child. Never yell or use sarcasm.

As a parent, you have three important tasks in keeping the lines of communication open with your children:

1. Stay alert to opportunities to communicate with your children.
2. Become a student of your kids, learning the unique ways they ask for attention.
3. Pray that God will sensitize you to hear your children's calls for attention when they come. Responding to those cries can do wonders to develop communication.

Which of these three actions will you work on this week?

RAISING YOUR CQ (COMMUNICATION QUOTIENT)

One of my initial goals in counseling is to get people to open up, to share what's going on. They will not feel comfortable until they feel somewhat secure in the environment. When a husband and a wife come in, for example, my sensitivity is higher toward the husband. I want him to know I'm not going to embarrass him in front of his wife. As security builds, the wall comes down; and he begins to reveal what's really on his mind with their marriage. A secure foundation is essential for meaningful communication. I might confront a husband on an issue but not before I've built credibility in communicating with him.

You must establish a similar foundation of security and trust with your kid before honesty has a chance. There is no secret formula that produces instant closeness. However, we can foster communication potential by spending time together, cultivating trust, and showing interest in our kids' lives. Building communication potential makes genuine conversation and closeness more likely.

> "Adolescents sometimes say, 'My friends listen to me, but my parents only hear me talk.' Often they are right. Familiarity breeds inattention."[6]
>
> —*Psychologist Laurence Steinberg*

Communication doesn't happen in a vacuum. If you want to have a meaningful relationship with your child, start developing a pattern of security and trust. Notice how the following components build on one another.

- Good communication comes as two parties open up.
- Opening up comes from trust.
- Trust comes from confidence in each other.
- Confidence comes from security.
- Security comes from an environment of safety, an atmosphere that says, "I am genuinely interested in you as a person, not to control you, lay my agenda on you, or preach you a sermon. I am on your side. I believe in you and want the best for you."

These practices are better shown to your kids than told to them. In her teens Jennifer and I would often play tennis. The fact that she played on her high-school team was a good excuse to keep the old man in shape. Driving to and from the courts gave us some good talk time. Sometimes we would have a burger after the workout.

Once Jen was dating a guy who was … well, let's say he was a little short in character compared to the man she eventually married. (OK, he was a lot short of David!) Our times together became the perfect vehicle to have deep conversations about this relationship. My interest and investment in one part of Jen's life (tennis) cultivated the security she needed to open up in more personal areas. In the end Jennifer made her own decision about "Mr. Character" (and she made a good one too!). But I was able to share my opinions and convictions because she knew I cared about all of her life, not just the guy she dated.

Natalie and I love to work complicated puzzles. We spend hours fitting pieces, laughing, philosophizing, speaking Spanish (her more than me), theologizing, and dreaming while looking for just the right one of three hundred pieces of sky. The whole time we work, we are building two foundations—one for the puzzle and one for communication. Sometimes we don't talk about anything significant. Yet even the most mundane conversation builds confidence and security in the relationship, allowing more serious talks to happen down the road. Sometimes communication is spelled t-i-m-e.

Today Natalie is away at college, but our times together continue. Our weekly phone conversations are on Monday nights—late, of course. (When else? She's in college; and besides, we are both night owls.) The first few minutes are always filled with sarcasm, a corny joke, or Dad carrying the Spanish conversation as far as he can! Then we move to the deeper issues of life and always end with a reminder of God's work in and plans for her life. These weekly talks have gone on for years, and I greatly cherish them.

Jen is a married young adult, but we frequently meet for Thursday lunches. We talk about work, sports, ministry, politics, and anything else rattling around in that passionate mind of hers.

The raising of Jennifer and Natalie is over. Now they consult us only if they choose to. But the time we've spent together lets them know they can still come to us with anything. The door of communication is still open.

Check the statements that characterize your communication with your children.

☐ I spend a lot of time talking with them.
☐ I use our conversation to cultivate trust and security.
☐ I show interest in their lives.

What are some activities you can do with your children to create opportunities for genuine communication?

Every conversation with your child affects the next one. You are either building communication potential or tearing it down. Show interest in your children's world. They realize you don't know everything about MySpace and texting. However, they will know you care about them. On the contrary, if you disrespect their thoughts and put them down, they will doubt your sincerity when you try to talk with them, and your next conversation will be less meaningful.

LEVELS OF COMMUNICATION

You can experience several levels of communication with your children. We learned most of these from marriage-enrichment leaders David and Vera Mace, but you will also find them helpful in understanding the way you communicate as a family.[7]

Level 1: small talk. This is where most of us live—conversation about the day-to-day stuff of life. Most of our communication is at this level. You want a healthy dose of small talk in your family. How we handle the ordinary, everyday stuff of life sets the tone for reaching the extraordinary levels of communication you want with your children (see Deut. 6:20-21).

For example, you are teaching your child how to throw a ball, cast a fishing pole, or bake a cake. But right in the middle of reviewing a ball-tossing technique, your child asks a question about life. If you are alert to the opportunity, you can respond, "Look at my nose. God has a plan for your life." Small talk—lots of it—is the beginning point of good communication and great adventures.

Deuteronomy 6:20-21
"When your son asks you in the future, 'What is the meaning of the decrees, statutes, and ordinances, which the LORD our God has commanded you?' tell him, 'We were slaves of Pharaoh in Egypt, but the LORD brought us out of Egypt with a strong hand.' "

Describe your favorite small-talk activity with your kids.

Level 2: sting talk. This unhealthy communication style contains little barbs of sarcasm and manipulation that can hurt deeply. Work to eliminate these from your family at all costs. They seem innocent enough, but over time they take on a toxic nature that shuts down healthy communication. Always remember, sarcasm and hateful talk are never productive (see Eph. 4:29).

Ephesians 4:29
"No rotten talk should come from your mouth, but only what is good for the building up of someone in need, in order to give grace to those who hear."

Examples of sting talk:
- "If only you were more like your sister ..."
- "You never do anything right."
- "I wish you would just go away and leave me alone."
- "Would you stop asking so many questions."
- "It figures. I didn't think you could."

Identify a time someone used sting talk with you. How did it affect you?

Watch for these poisonous remarks in your home. When they happen (after all, we are all human), immediately stop and deal with them. Say, "I'm sorry. I'm tired, and I shouldn't have said that." You can always recognize these statements because they sting, and someone feels the pain.

    Level 3: search talk. This level is reached when your children share their dreams and goals. Every great adventure has dreams. Where would you like to go? What would you like to be? What would you like to build? Where would you like to sing, work, travel, minister, and so forth?

"You can't have a dream come true without a dream."

This type of communication is fun and allows every member of the family to stretch and grow. Every child needs to feel the freedom to dream. We as adults can learn much from the wonder of a child who is just being a child. Let yourself be captivated by the magic of pretending and adventure as only a child can experience it.

Building search talk into your children at an early age will allow them to open their eyes and hearts to all God wants to do in their lives as they move into adulthood (see Matt. 19:14). It can help them discover their passions as they seek to learn God's plans for their lives.

Matthew 19:14
"Jesus said, 'Leave the children alone, and don't try to keep them from coming to Me, because the kingdom of heaven is made up of people like this.' "

What dreams have you heard your children express lately?

How can your talks with your kids encourage them to dream big dreams?

What dream of your own could you share with your child?

Level 4: straight talk. The deepest level of communication is straight talk. This is sharing matters of the heart—feelings. One guideline in our home was that feelings are not right or wrong; they just are. God has given us a full range of emotions to express. All great adventures allow children to experience this full range of feelings. As you build healthy talk into your home, you will find that sharing feelings is a powerful way to teach.

For example, anger is often a secondary emotion and can be easily misunderstood. When a child (or an adult) seems very angry, our first response is to stop the anger. After all, it usually isn't a very pretty sight. "Jamie, you shouldn't be angry." "Caleb, go to your room until you get over your anger."

How do you react when your children express anger?

I was counseling a pastor whose teenage son was going through a very rebellious period, resulting in major tension between father and son. The father expressed his anger, but the truth was that he was deeply hurting over his son's choices. I told him to share his hurt with his son. He said, "But Rodney, that's how I share my hurt—through my anger!"

Granted, there is time to let the anger cool off so that you can talk. However, don't miss the what's-behind-the-anger opportunity with your children, whether they are 2 or 15. Often you will discover gold as you gain insight into your child's expanding world, such as fear, hurt, insecurity, or uncertainty. What a relief it can be to a kid, however, when he is allowed to express some or all of these feelings in an environment of respect and trust.

A feelings level of communication is packed full of opportunities for you to teach your child. Let your home be a place where feelings can be openly expressed.
- **Preschool:** "Daddy, I'm scared of the dark." "Mommy, I love music."
- **Elementary age:** "Joey hurt me when he called me four-eyes." "I really love my science class."
- **Middle school:** "I'm ugly." "I'm stupid." "I think I like this boy in my gym class."
- **Adolescent:** "I get so angry when you say that." "I feel a lot of compassion for lost people."
- **College:** "I'm afraid to go away to school." "I'm excited to go away to school."

What feelings are your children expressing now?

If they aren't telling you how they feel, how could you encourage them to share openly?

Level 5: tough talk. Parents, one of our jobs is to have the tough conversations with our children. Sometimes they mess up, and it's up to us to confront them with truth. It is part of preparing them for life with God (see Prov. 1:8-9).

Avoiding sting talk doesn't mean you avoid discipline. It means even in the middle of tension and disobedience, you are firm. At the same time, you strive to show Christ to your children while helping them learn from their mistakes:

- "Son, I love you too much to let you do this."
- "You've broken my trust, and you will need to build it back. Until then I'm going to require more of you."
- "Sin always has a consequence. I can't fix this one for you."
- "You will not talk to your mother like that."

Proverbs 1:8-9
"Listen, my son, to your father's instruction, and don't reject your mother's teaching, for they will be a garland of grace on your head and a gold chain around your neck."

Which levels of communication does your family do well? Check all that apply.

☐ Small talk
☐ Sting talk
☐ Search talk
☐ Straight talk
☐ Tough talk

Circle the level that you most need to work on.

TEACHING SPIRITUAL TRUTH AS YOU GO

One of the most amazing experiences we have as children of God is to talk to Him and have Him speak to us. God has planned an amazing talk system to communicate with His children. When we talk to God, He hears us and speaks to us through His Spirit who lives in us, through prayer, and through His Word. Building a strong talk system with your children helps them grow and develop honest, open communication with God, which is essential for life with Him.

Read the following Scriptures and match them with the correct instructions about prayer.

     ___ 1. Psalm 5:1-3   a. Pray all the time.

     ___ 2. Philippians 4:6   b. Instead of worrying, pray.

     ___ 3. 1 Thessalonians 5:17   c. Ask God for help every day.

Psalm 5:1-3, The Message

"Listen, GOD! Please, pay attention! Can you make sense of these ramblings, my groans and cries? King-God, I need your help. Every morning you'll hear me at it again. Every morning I lay out the pieces of my life on your altar."

Philippians 4:6

"Don't worry about anything, but in everything, through prayer and petition with thanksgiving let your requests be made known to God."

1 Thessalonians 5:17

"Pray constantly."

When you let your children hear and see you pray, you prepare them for life on their own. Real, honest, open prayer. Prayers of petition, prayers of thanksgiving, truly going to God with all the stuff of life, big and small—all this should be as natural to us as talking to one another. God says to us, "Just talk to Me." Talking to God gives us perspective on everything else in life!

Check all the statements that describe your prayer life as a parent.

☐ I pray a blessing before meals.
☐ I cry out to God about all my needs as a parent and about my children's needs.
☐ I make time for consistent prayer.
☐ I encourage my children to pray.
☐ I do not pray regularly.
☐ I pray about the big things but not everyday needs.
☐ Other:

Stop and pray now about any changes you need to make in your prayer life and especially about teaching your children to rely on God through prayer.

FROM LIFEWAY RESEARCH

Only 17 percent of parents say the quality of COMMUNICATION among family members is excellent, while most (68 percent) call it either good or very good.

16% Sixteen percent rate the amount of time the whole family spends together as excellent, while most (65 percent) rate it either good or very good.

Almost all parents say, "I love you," "You can do this," and "I'm proud of you" once a month or more; but 3 out of 10 also say, "I'm disappointed in you" that frequently.

53% Just 53 percent of families pray together once a month or more, and only 31 percent have religious devotionals or studies together that often. Yet over 9 out of 10 watch television together once a month or more.[8]

THE PARENT ADVENTURE PLAN

What can you do this week with your child that says, "Let's talk"?
1.
2.
3.

What new talk systems do you want to add to your family?

What can you share with your child about God's work in your life through prayer?

What Scripture verse can you share with your children this week that will teach them about the importance of talking to God? See page 94 for ideas.

PRAYER FOCUS

"Father, thank You for allowing me to talk to You anytime and anywhere. I am staggered by the reality that I can even be in Your presence. Thank You for Jesus, who makes it possible for us to talk. O Father, use me today to teach my child to talk to me but more importantly to talk to You. Again, I give them to You. Use me to get them ready for life with You. May they see You in me today."

PAIN HAPPENS

chapter five

session five GROUP EXPERIENCE

GET TO KNOW YOUR GROUP

DISCUSS what you discovered from your parent adventure after reading chapter 4, "Let's Talk."

READ the following list of painful experiences. Share what immediately comes to mind when you read each phrase.

- Car crash
- Broken heart
- Hospital stay
- Death of a pet
- Stained shirt
- Embarrassing fall
- Foot-in-mouth moment
- Bad haircut
- Fight with a friend
- Bad grade

WARM-UP

- Describe a physically painful experience that happened to your child.

- How did you know what to do?

WATCH DVD

- Watch DVD session 5.
- What stood out to you in this session?

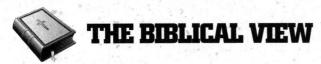

THE BIBLICAL VIEW

Psalm 51:1-4

"Have mercy on me, O God, according to your unfailing love; according to your great compassion blot out my transgressions. Wash away all my iniquity and cleanse me from my sin. For I know my transgressions, and my sin is always before me. Against you, you only, have I sinned and done what is evil in your sight, so that you are proved right when you speak and justified when you judge."

- How can you help your child navigate through the pain caused by sinful choices?

Matthew 26:36-39

"Jesus went with his disciples to a place called Gethsemane, and he said to them, 'Sit here while I go over there and pray.' He took Peter and the two sons of Zebedee along with him, and he began to be sorrowful and troubled. Then he said to them, 'My soul is overwhelmed with sorrow to the point of death. Stay here and keep watch with me.' Going a little farther, he fell with his face to the ground and prayed, 'My Father, if it is possible, may this cup be taken from me. Yet not as I will, but as you will.' "

- How can you help your child endure the pain that comes from doing the right thing?

- Share responses to the activity on page 108.

THE ADVENTURE

- How can pain help your children grow spiritually?

- How can you empower your children to handle painful situations?

- Why is it dangerous to protect your child from all pain?

- Describe a painful circumstance in your life that made you who you are today.

- How can you point your child to God even when you don't have answers to the why questions?

- How can your children learn to handle pain by watching you?

- How can you model for your kids victory in pain?

- What painful situations do your children face now? How can you point them to God in the middle of the hurt?

CLOSING THOUGHTS

Pray that God will guide you as a parent to help your children navigate through pain. Pray that your children will grow close to God and trust Him during painful times.

NEXT WEEK

"Celebrate!" will teach you how to regularly celebrate God's work in your life and in the lives of your children as an act of worship.

PAIN HAPPENS

chapter five

Matthew 6:34

"Each day has enough trouble of its own."

Most of the Wilsons' craziest adventures happened in the Great Smoky Mountains, our family's vacation spot while the girls were growing up. Every summer we hiked trails, climbed rocks, picnicked, camped, and played miniature golf. Our favorite tradition was always on the itinerary—Cades Cove biking. Even before the girls could ride their own bikes, they loved to sit in their baby seats and ride along behind Selma and me. Biking through God's creation provided a peaceful, soothing family excursion … that is, until Jen started riding her own bike. Sayonara, serenity.

Jennifer was six years old, and her feet barely touched the pedals. Still we agreed that she was old enough to ride alone, and we assured her that all would be well. Unfortunately, we discovered that the steep hills that challenge most adults terrify small children.

Riding down one hill with Natalie, our four-year-old, strapped in the seat behind me, I heard Selma scream. I turned around to see a horrified look on Jen's face. She had lost control of her bike and was now barreling down the hill, both legs straight out, eyes closed, and the pedals whirling faster and faster. She shot toward a nearby oak tree like a heat-seeking missile.

In that instant I had 1/10 of a second to decide which daughter I would sacrifice. I could drop my bike and Natalie by default, or I could watch Jen smash against a tree. I quickly released my bike and stepped over to snatch Jen off her runaway bike-train. Her velocity spun us around a full 360 degrees.

Meanwhile, Natalie, minding her own business as she enjoyed the beauty of the mountains, suddenly crashed onto the gravel road. For some reason she started to cry! Thankfully, she suffered only a small scratch.

After a few moments the family settled down. Natalie stopped crying, and Jen got back on her bike. We rallied and continued the 12-mile loop, spotting some deer and enjoying the peaceful scenery once again.

That night reality sank in. I remembered feeling unnerved when I saw Jennifer's face. She was going to crash into that tree at three hundred miles an hour, it seemed, or Natalie was going to have a quick meeting with the road. Either way, pain stared my family in the face. I told everyone I was sorry for Nat's pain but didn't know what to do. Selma and Jennifer assured me I did the right thing, because Jen could have been seriously injured. It took Natalie a little longer, but she finally agreed. Sometimes it's tough being a four-year-old!

Describe an incident that brought pain to one of your children.

How did that incident change your view of parenting?

Through painful experiences like this, we had to recognize and accept that pain would be a reality in our family; but we determined not to let pain or the fear of pain rob us of the joy of parenting. Our family has experienced more than a decade of mountain adventures. What if we had decided to avoid all pain by staying home and never discovering the beauty of God's creation? I think of all the wonders we would have missed—the sunrises, the thrill of catching a fish, the awe of seeing a bear in a tree, the grace of deer running through the meadows, the wonder of waking up and finding ourselves enveloped in the mist of clouds, the campfires, and the glow of kerosene lamps as we talked of life and God.

Our adventures in God's creation almost always cost us some pain or occasional discomfort. On another Smokies trip we were climbing a huge river rock when I slipped and fell, injuring my hip. On one six-mile mountain hike,

Natalie, who was seven, started crying; sat down; and said, "I just can't go on." She was exhausted, so we rallied around her and rested for about an hour. When we finally convinced her to continue, the campsite was just around the bend. Years later on another bike ride, Selma and I experienced pain—the pain of getting older, especially when our teenage girls had to stop and wait for us at the top of every hill!

A PARENT'S PROBLEM WITH PAIN

When Selma and I recall the incident with the runaway bike, I tend to go into guilt mode, somehow feeling it was my fault. Her response is always "Yes, Natalie was hurt, but not as bad as Jennifer could have been."

Have you ever felt guilty when your children got hurt?
□ Yes   □ No

If so, why do you think you felt guilty?

The reality is that whether on a vacation adventure or in everyday life, parents can never prevent all of our children's pain. This can be hard for parents to accept because it's natural for us to want to protect our children. Think about it. From the day a baby is born, safety is a priority. We block stairways, put breakables into storage, and wish we could run an FBI background check on everyone who wants to hold our baby. Parents are responsible for protecting and defending our children. We naturally want to build a safety net—spiritually, emotionally, socially, and physically—so that nothing can ever hurt or scar our children. Although safety is a critical issue for our children, when taken to the extreme, it can hurt our children more than it helps.

"Don't handicap your children by making their lives easy."[1]

—*Robert A. Heinlein*

No creature understands pain like a caterpillar. Trapped inside the cocoon, it must slowly and painfully build muscle by ripping through the cocoon wall. A child who comes along and opens the cocoon damages the butterfly by stunting its wings. The caterpillar gets instant relief, but it will never fly.

Ironically, one of the greatest gifts you can give your kids is the ability to handle pain. You can help your children pray, struggle, and wrestle through the pain of life until one day they are strong enough to stand on their own—ready to fly. Instead of running away or fixing every problem, prepare your kids for life with God by teaching them spiritual truth in the middle of the pain.

> Sometimes life hurts. Sometimes life is not fair. You are not necessarily a bad parent when your kid has a painful experience.

Describe a positive outcome of a painful situation one of your children has experienced.

PERSPECTIVE IN THE PAIN

Pain happens in every stage of childhood:

- **Preschool:** skinned knees, death of a bug or frog or fish
- **Elementary age:** loss of a game, bike wreck, death of a pet
- **Preadolescent:** betrayal of a friend, ridicule of peers
- **Adolescent:** death of a grandparent, failing a test, first breakup
- **College:** not being accepted by the college of choice, broken heart, death of a friend

When kids are young, it's hard for them to see beyond their pain. One skinned knee, and the world is over. In adolescence it's the broken heart or the mean MySpace post that shatters their world. One way you can help is to offer spiritual perspective, helping your kids see pain as an opportunity to grow with God.

Read below some of Jesus' teachings about pain.
Mark the statements *T* for *true* or *F* for *false*.

___ Christians are immune from pain.
___ Christians can expect to have pain in this world.
___ Jesus has won the victory over suffering.

Matthew 6:34
"Each day has enough trouble of its own."

John 16:33
"You will have suffering in this world. Be courageous! I have conquered the world."

Jesus promised us that we would have trouble in the world. None of us are immune from pain. Jesus also reminded us that He is Lord over every pain. He has overcome the world.

I got the call. Jennifer was hysterically crying on the other end of the line. Flashes of possible crises were running through my mind when I heard her say, "Mom, I didn't get the lead part in the musical!" Now, mind you, she got a part, just not the lead part, the one she had auditioned for. To top it off, one of her friends got the part instead of her. In Jennifer's adolescent world this ranked right up there as a major crisis! There was nothing I could do to stop her pain. I felt that helpless feeling all parents sometimes feel.

Identify a time when one of your children experienced a disappointment.

How did you respond to your child's hurt? Check all that apply.

☐ Cried with him or her
☐ Felt helpless
☐ Prayed with him or her
☐ Discussed ways to learn from the experience
☐ Blamed him or her
☐ Got angry at the source of the pain
☐ Other:

When your child hurts, you hurt; soon I found myself crying right along with Jennifer (and wanting to call her obviously deaf music director). Instead, I called a dear friend to give me counsel. What does a mom do when she can't fix it? We hurt together as a family and listened to Jen talk about it for days (and days). Eventually, we were able to discuss key truths—life is not always fair, but God would use this truth to strengthen Jen's trust in Him. The musical went on, and she did great in her part. Most importantly, she grew through it all. God was shaping her.

> "Too often we give children answers to remember rather than problems to solve."[2]—*Roger Lewin*

The pain of life isn't fun for us or our kids. Yet pain can provide many teachable moments. "Sarah, remember what happened when you touched Mommy's straightener?" Three-year-old Sarah instantly recalls the lesson learned from a burned finger. Other lessons can range from working through preadolescent peer-group betrayal to a 17-year-old's learning the importance of oil to a car engine.

As parents, our role is to be the facilitator of those lessons—to point out the larger picture, the reasons for the experience, and the importance of seeking God in their pain. Parents can help their kids work through the pain and grow in the process. The big-picture view is not just salvaging an experience or making the most of a tough day but pointing your children to God. True spiritual growth takes place when they learn to trust God in their pain.

Do you point your children to God when they hurt?
☐ Yes ☐ No

Sometimes your children will hurt, and you won't have an answer. A lot of the world's sorrow defies explanation, advice, and reason. If you can't explain the why of a painful situation, you can still explain the who. Saturate your counsel with the power of God's Word, which is rich in comfort and strength during times of sadness. Show your children God's promise never to leave us (see Heb. 13:5-6). Teach them that God is still in control, and He has a plan through the hurt (see Jer. 29:11). Remind them of His promise that He has already overcome the world (see John 16:33). Allow them to grieve, but gently speak spiritual truth into their lives.

Hebrews 13:5-6
"He Himself has said, I will never leave you or forsake you.
Therefore, we may boldly say:
The Lord is my helper;
I will not be afraid.
What can man do to me?"

Even when you're all out of encouragement, God's Word is full of hope. In Christ nothing can defeat us. Pain does not have the power to cripple us spiritually or emotionally. This world is not our home, and one day we will live pain-free in the presence of our Creator. You can live these truths in front of your child and speak them even in the hard and painful places of life.

What Scripture passages have you used or could you use to counsel your children when they suffer?

In Luke 8:22-25 Jesus, the Master Teacher, created an excellent teachable moment in a painfully frightening experience. One day Jesus and His disciples were crossing a lake in a boat, and Jesus fell asleep. When a huge storm came, it appeared that the boat would sink. They were going down for the last time when the disciples shouted at Jesus out of fear. Jesus woke up, calmed the sea, and asked them where their faith had gone.

What lessons do you think the disciples learned through this experience?

Jesus used this incident to teach at least three points.
1. Storms will happen in your life, but I will be with you through them.
2. I am stronger than any storm you will encounter.
3. Even when you don't see Me working right away (on your time schedule), trust Me in the storm.

Jesus seized an opportunity to teach lessons the disciples would remember for the rest of their lives. These lessons would not have been so memorable and meaningful to them if they not experienced the pain of paralyzing fear in the storm. But when they called on Jesus, they witnessed His power at work and learned a life-changing message about faith.

LOOKING TO GOD'S WORD

Teaching your children to look to God in their pain includes showing them how His Word relates to our lives. By reading the stories of other hurting people, we learn about God's character and how to respond in difficult situations. We see patterns of faith, endurance, and hope in the middle of suffering. When your children are small, you might not be able to go into great depth about suffering, but you can teach them that God cares for us when we hurt. As your children grow, point out specific Bible stories or characters that might bring encouragement during a tough time. Show them how to study God's Word consistently so that when pain happens, they will have already developed the habit of listening to God speak through His Word.

God's Word gives us many examples of people who looked to God when they experienced pain. Here is an approach you can take to help your children explore ways biblical characters dealt with their pain. Read together a passage of Scripture and ask who, what, and why questions to help your children identify key facts. Then ask a question that prompts the family to discuss how the person turned to God in suffering and what we can learn from this Bible character. Here are some examples.

Psalm 51—the pain of sin

- Who? King David
- What? David had an affair, killed his mistress's husband, and lost his child. His sin created a barrier between himself and God.
- Why? David gave us a great example of repentance and restoration. His son Solomon became the wisest king in the history of the world.
- Family-discussion question: How did David respond after he sinned? What can we learn from him?

2 Corinthians 12:7-10—possibly physical pain

- Who? Paul
- What? A thorn in the flesh
- Why? Though Paul begged the Lord to remove his pain, God did not. Instead, He responded, "My grace is sufficient for you, for power is perfected in weakness" (v. 9). Paul praised God and acknowledged His power in his weakness.
- Family-discussion question: Why do you think God wanted Paul to keep the thorn? What can we learn from Paul's response to God?

John 11:1-30—the pain of losing a loved one

- Who? Mary and Martha
- What? The death of their brother Lazarus
- Why? Jesus wept alongside Mary and Martha. He eventually displayed his power as "the resurrection and the life" (v. 25) and raised Lazarus from the grave.
- Family-discussion question: Why does death hurt family members so much? What can we learn from Jesus about death?

Matthew 26:36-39—pain that results from obeying God

- Who? Jesus
- What? Anticipating the agony of the cross in the garden of Gethsemane
- Why? Jesus knew the pain He was about to endure. He asked God if there was another way; yet He surrendered to His Father's will, bringing salvation to us.
- Family-discussion question: What can we learn from Jesus as He faced the pain of the cross?

Select one of the previous examples that you think would speak to your children. Use the process suggested to study the passage with them. What lessons did your children learn from this biblical example?

What lessons did you learn in this discussion with your children?

TEACHING YOUR KIDS TO HANDLE PAIN

In addition to crying out to God and looking to His Word, children learn to handle pain by watching you. When you turn to God in the storms of life, your children will learn when to seek God's Word and how to cling to Him during difficult situations. Your children will see you face painful and unfair situations such as the death of a parent, the loss of a job, or conflict at work. When they see you praying, consulting God's Word, and pressing on, they'll get firsthand proof that trusting God works.

Check the ways you usually handle crises as a parent.

☐ Pray and trust in God
☐ Have an emotional meltdown
☐ Feed on God's Word
☐ Seek to escape the discomfort
☐ Other:

You don't have to be perfect in pain. Neither do you need to create needless anxiety by sharing every detail with your children. But honest communication about walking with God during your crisis can speak volumes to them about how to seek God and cast their cares on Him during tough times (see 1 Pet. 5:6-7).

1 Peter 5:6-7
"Humble yourselves therefore under the mighty hand of God, so that
He may exalt you in due time, casting all your care upon Him, because
He cares about you."

When your children watch you going through pain in a healthy manner, they witness the way a believer stays faithful to God through the storm. Don't misunderstand; you don't need to put on a fake smile and an "Everything's fine" front. Your kids can see that you hurt deeply but still honor your commitment to God and His Word in the middle of the pain. You also don't have to hurt alone. It's great when your kids see you lean on your spouse, friends, counselors, and mentors during tough times. Later in their lives when pain comes, your children will take courage from the way you modeled spiritual wisdom and strength in your storms.

We are currently healing from a painful time in our family. Rodney's dad suffered a major stroke more than a year ago and recently passed away. For months he was completely paralyzed, unable to speak or move. His mother, who suffers from crippling arthritis, spends most of her time in a wheelchair. She is weak, and most of her days are filled with pain. In the middle of this very rough time, God was and is so real to us. He has answered many prayers. Dad was blessed with a wonderful care facility that has a loving staff—a miracle. God led us to a wonderful Christian woman to stay with Mom at night—another miracle.

There is so much pain we don't understand, but we are learning every day to trust God. One of the most beautiful things for us and our children to see was how Mom loved Dad during this painful time. Dad couldn't give Mom anything— not a smile, not a word, not a touch—but she visited him every day. After 63 years of marriage Mom still got dressed up, touched him with her crippled hands, and whispered words of love to him. She tucked the sheets around him and fussed over him, making sure the nurses knew that he was her treasured husband.

Painful. Beautiful. I am so thankful that our adult daughters, one married herself now, saw a model of marriage and love as only our God can give—unconditional love, agape love.

When NFL coach Tony Dungy was fired from one head coaching position, he said, "I think people look more closely at our actions in the rough times, when the emotions are raw and our guard is down. That's when our true character shows and we find out if our faith is real. If I'm going to call myself a Christian, I have to honor Jesus in the disappointments, too."[3]

If you are facing hardship now, check one or more ways you will try to model for your children faithfulness to God during this time.

☐ Pray and claim the promises in God's Word
☐ Trust God
☐ Seek the counsel of others
☐ Maintain spiritual perspective
☐ Other:

THE PAIN OF A PARENT'S REGRET

When our girls were little, I always intended to build them a tree house in our backyard. They kept asking for one; but time and life kept slipping away, and the tree house never happened. (My only hope of redemption is to build it for the grandkids; but trust me, no promises!)

All parents have tree-house stories in their past—times when they made mistakes in parenting, let their children down, or inadvertently hurt them. We all do it sooner or later. Like pain, it is not a matter of whether regret comes; rather, when it does, how do we manage it?

If we dwell on our past mistakes, they can cripple us, rendering us helpless as parents. Confidence can bottom out every time we think of what we should or shouldn't have done in parenting.

What are some regrets you have with your kids?

How do these regrets affect your parenting?

When you find yourself about to drown in the vat of regret, here are two responses that can help.

Face the regret. To fight regret, sometimes you have to be man or woman enough to look your kids right in the eye (maybe ask them to look at your nose) and ask them to forgive you. There is power in a humble apology. Seeking forgiveness tells your kids that you know you are not perfect and mess up sometimes.

A parent can blow it at any stage. About two months after our first daughter married, Jen and David visited our home late one night. Selma had already gone to bed. Jen was laughing with her sister, Natalie—in my opinion, a little too loudly. I stated in a soft but fatherly, stern (perhaps condescending) voice that if they didn't hush, they would wake their mom.

I immediately saw the look in Jennifer's eye and knew I had crossed a line. I also knew I would never have spoken to any other wife like that in front of her husband. The third thing I knew was that I would have to apologize to her, and I did in front of her husband. (For a guy who had just blown it, I sure knew a lot!) And just as she had done for the past 20-plus years, she quickly forgave me.

When necessary, no matter how long it has been, seek forgiveness from your kid. Yes, it is tough and risky. You will be vulnerable, for sure. And yet you will make a huge statement of honesty and love when you take that step.

Our pastor, Pat Hood, reminds us every week that he sins; and like Paul in Philippians 3:13, he says, "I've not yet taken hold of it" (I don't have it all together). Every time he mentions something like that, it builds credibility and connects with people. When parents ask for forgiveness from their children, it builds the same credibility. It connects with the kids and helps parents overcome the pain of regret.

Identify anything for which you need to ask forgiveness from your children.

Are you ready to ask them to forgive you?
☐ Yes ☐ No

Beware of the enemy. We have an enemy who wants us to fail as parents. He does not want us to experience the abundant life and the parent adventure that God has planned for us. God's purpose in our lives is for Him to be gloried in our lives. Satan's purpose is to rob God of His glory! One way he tries to defeat us is by spotlighting our past faults and getting us to dwell on them.

First Peter 5:8 puts it this way: "Be sober! Be on the alert! Your adversary the Devil is prowling around like a roaring lion, looking for anyone he can devour." And his most effective weapon? Deception. Here is the way Jesus described him: "When he [the Devil] tells a lie, he speaks from his own nature, because he is a liar and the father of liars" (John 8:44). Satan tries to make us believe what is not true. If our guard is not up and we are not walking closely with the Lord, who is Truth, we can find ourselves buying the lies the enemy throws at us. Regret can derail our parent adventure with God.

> Parents are not irresponsible because their children have pain. The irresponsibility comes when they don't teach them the lesson found in the pain.

How can we withstand Satan's efforts to deceive us? With the truth of God's Word. Just as Jesus used Scripture when combating the deceiver (see Matt. 4:1-11), so can we. We can overcome our mistakes and regrets by applying the truth of God's Word.

Here are some examples of deceit the enemy can throw at us and some scriptural truths you can use to respond to his attacks.

- *Deceit:* You can't do anything as a parent because of the way you've treated your kids in the past. *Truth:* "If we confess our sins, He is faithful and righteous to forgive us our sins and to cleanse us from all unrighteousness" (1 John 1:9).
- *Deceit:* Who do you think you are trying to build relationship with your kid? Don't you remember how you yelled at her just last week? *Truth:* "If anyone is in Christ, there is a new creation; old things have passed away, and look, new things have come" (2 Cor. 5:17).
- *Deceit:* Why are you of all people trying to teach your kids anything about God? You lied to your kids, remember? *Truth:* "One thing I do: forgetting what is behind and reaching forward to what is ahead, I pursue as my goal the prize promised by God's heavenly call in Christ Jesus" (Phil. 3:13-14). "No condemnation now exists for those in Christ Jesus" (Rom. 8:1).
- *Deceit:* You must believe my view of you—that you will never be a good parent—because you've believed it too long. *Truth:* "The One who is in you is greater than the one who is in the world" (1 John 4:4).

Go back and circle the biblical truth you need most in your parenting now. Then pray and ask God to help you believe His truth for your job as a parent. Ask Him to help you make a new start as you move forward in His strength and wisdom.

TEACHING SPIRITUAL TRUTH AS YOU GO

Let's review our focal Scripture for our study, this time from *The Message:*

Deuteronomy 6:5-7, The Message
"Love GOD, your God, with your whole heart: love him with all that's in you, love him with all you've got! Write these commandments that I've given you today on your hearts. Get them inside of you and then get them inside your children. Talk about them wherever you are, sitting at home or walking in the street; talk about them from the time you get up in the morning to when you fall into bed at night."

It's easy to love God with our whole hearts when life is great. However, we grow in our relationship with Him when we continue loving Him in the pain, even when we don't understand His plans. During these times you have the opportunity to show your children that God's love is strong enough to get you through any situation.

When storms come against your family, you and your children can be prepared to weather them if God's commandments are written on your hearts. And when the enemy attacks, it's easier to fight if you already have an arsenal of Scripture ready to fire. God's Word builds an anchor of hope and a shield of faith around us during times of pain.

In the middle of the pain your family will inevitably experience in life, impress your children with biblical truths like the following.

As you read these Scriptures, underline who God is when we face trials. Circle what He does for us in times of trouble.

- "No one will be able to stand against you as long as you live. I will be with you just as I was with Moses. I will never leave you nor forsake you" (Josh. 1:5).
- "I have told you these things so that in Me you may have peace. You will have suffering in this world. Be courageous! I have conquered the world" (John 16:33).

- "The eternal God is your refuge, and underneath are the everlasting arms. He will drive out your enemy before you, saying, 'Destroy him!' " (Deut. 33:27, NIV).
- "You are my hiding place; You protect me from trouble. You surround me with joyful shouts of deliverance" (Ps. 32:7).
- "The righteous cry out, and the LORD hears, and delivers them from all their troubles" (Ps. 34:17).
- "God is our refuge and strength, a helper who is always found in times of trouble" (Ps. 46:1).
- "Do you not know? Have you not heard? Yahweh is the everlasting God, the Creator of the whole earth. He never grows faint or weary; there is no limit to His understanding. He gives strength to the weary and strengthens the powerless" (Isa. 40:28-29).
- "Peace I leave with you. My peace I give to you. I do not give to you as the world gives. Your heart must not be troubled or fearful" (John 14:27).
- "If God is for us, who is against us?" (Rom. 8:31).
- "Be sober! Be on the alert! Your adversary the Devil is prowling around like a roaring lion, looking for anyone he can devour. Resist him, firm in the faith, knowing that the same sufferings are being experienced by your brothers in the world. Now the God of all grace, who called you to His eternal glory in Christ Jesus, will personally restore, establish, strengthen, and support you after you have suffered a little" (1 Pet. 5:8-10).

FROM LIFEWAY RESEARCH

3/4 About three out of four parents say they try to keep their own pain away from their children.

Six out of 10 parents want their children TO EXPERIENCE pain and disappointment so that they can learn from it, while 4 out of 10 try to protect them whenever they can.

28% Twenty-eight percent of parents agree they feel a lot of regret about what they've done as parents.[4]

THE PARENT ADVENTURE PLAN

What can you tell your children about how God has worked in your life through a painful experience?

Identify a child in your family who is currently experiencing pain.

What three things can you do to help him or her through this pain?
1.
2.
3.

What can you share with your children from God's Word to help them understand how God helps us through pain? See the passages on pages 116–17, as well as others in this chapter.

PRAYER FOCUS

"Father, You know how much I want to protect my children from the pain and heartbreak of this life, but I know I can't. Thank You for being with me through loss and pain that I have experienced. Just as You were with me, I know You will be with my children. I pray that You will protect them from the Evil One. Help me teach them the truth of who You are through every situation in life, including the hurt and disappointment they will face. Give me wisdom to point them to You. Let my children see You in me."

CELEBRATE!

chapter six

session six GROUP EXPERIENCE

GET TO KNOW YOUR GROUP

DISCUSS what you discovered from your parent adventure after reading chapter 5, "Pain Happens."

READ the following list, which contrasts what causes adults to celebrate versus what causes children to celebrate.

Adults celebrate:
- Finding a $100 bill
- A clean house
- Emptying our inbox
- Building our 401(k)
- Eating a steak inside a five-star restaurant

Children celebrate:
- Finding a quarter in the sandbox
- A clean diaper
- Emptying a bowl of spaghetti on their heads
- Building a sandcastle
- Eating a burger and fries inside a five-star plastic slide

WARM-UP

- Describe a time when your child got really excited about something small.

WATCH DVD

- Watch DVD session 6.
- What stood out to you in this session?

THE BIBLICAL VIEW

Luke 15:20-22

"While the son was still a long way off, his father saw him and was filled with compassion. He ran, threw his arms around his neck, and kissed him. The son said to him, 'Father, I have sinned against heaven and in your sight. I'm no longer worthy to be called your son.' But the father told his slaves, 'Quick! Bring out the best robe and put it on him; put a ring on his finger and sandals on his feet. Then bring the fattened calf and slaughter it, and let's celebrate with a feast, because this son of mine was dead and is alive again; he was lost and is found!' So they began to celebrate."

- How does it make you feel to know God celebrates over you?

- How does this reality change the way you see yourself?

Psalm 111:2-4

"The LORD's works are great, studied by all who delight in them. All that he does is splendid and majestic; His righteousness endures forever. He has caused His wonderful works to be remembered."

- How does God's work in your life inspire you to celebrate?

- How are you teaching your children to celebrate who God is and what He does?

 **THE ADVENTURE**

- Why is it important to celebrate with your children in little and big ways?

- What does a celebration home look and feel like?

- Turn to page 126 and read the list of causes for celebration in your children's lives. Name other ways to celebrate with your children.

- How can you build celebration into the daily routine of life?

- What life changes will your children soon experience, such as walking, talking, middle school, driving, or dating? How can you help them celebrate as they go through these transitions?

- What is something small you can celebrate this week with your family?

- How can you teach your children about God in the middle of that celebration?

 **CLOSING THOUGHTS**

Pray a prayer of celebration, thanking God for your children. Ask Him to help you make the most of daily opportunities to celebrate His work and blessings in your life.

CELEBRATE!

chapter six

2 Samuel 6:21

"I will celebrate before the LORD."

The last thing I expected was a party. It had been a long day and an even longer commute home. I was exhausted, and it was only Tuesday. I enjoyed coming home from the office, but I knew when I walked through the front door that work was hardly finished. Most evenings consisted of dinner, clean-up, baths for the girls, help with homework, then the bedtime routine. This particular night, however, was anything but typical. When I walked through the door, my mood was immediately transformed.

My girls—all three of them—had decided this night would be special. Decorations filled our living room and kitchen. The table was set with the good china. Celebration filled the air. On a weeknight! It wasn't anyone's birthday. I hadn't received a raise or promotion. They just wanted to celebrate an ordinary, everyday event—Daddy coming home!

When asked what she'd change about her life, an elderly woman said, "I'd use my good china much more often."

Think about a time when you were surprised by a celebration. How did it make you feel?

The celebrative atmosphere changed everything that evening. The tiredness of the day faded, and my spirit was lifted. I quickly caught the spirit of celebration my girls had created.

A TIME TO CELEBRATE

Ecclesiastes 3:4 says there is "a time to weep and a time to laugh; a time to mourn and a time to dance." Solomon emphasized the need for balance in our lives. Parents need to strike a balance with their families. Don't get swept away in the day-to-day routines of life. Instead, carve out frequent times and places to celebrate with your family.

When we look around our world, it's hard to find reasons to celebrate. Crises such as poverty, the economy, war, and immorality stare us in the face every day, not to mention our own family's trials and struggles. It might seem trivial or even irresponsible to spend time celebrating the little things together.

What do you think is the biggest challenge facing families today?

What specific challenges does your family face now?

In families there will always be things that need attention. The oil needs changing in your car. Your Internet connection is down again. (Been there.) And that slow drain in the bathtub—aughh! Your third-grader's teacher called a conference because she said he did what? Throw in day-to-day work problems, and you find yourself rapidly climbing the stress scale.

Clearly, the world is full of things we need to pay attention to. As parents, we have the responsibility to discuss age-appropriate issues with our children because God deeply cares about the world. We need to care for the poor, the hungry, the lonely, the sick, and the unsaved. Celebration, however, does not mean sweeping those concerns under the rug. Instead, celebration suggests there are some things worth taking time—in the middle of life—to recognize and enjoy. Sometimes for a moment, sometimes for a weekend, sometimes longer.

Matthew recorded the account of a woman who chose to celebrate Jesus. Much to the anger and confusion of the disciples, she broke an expensive jar of oil and washed his feet. Jesus responded to their frustrations by chiding, "You always have the poor with you" (26:11). Jesus wasn't dismissing the poor, but He was saying, "Yes, there will always be other concerns; but for this moment I want to celebrate this woman's gesture." Two thousand years later we still remember her act of worship and humility. When Jesus sets a celebration in motion, it sticks!

What is your family doing to celebrate Jesus?

Actually, life's hardships and challenges make celebration all the more necessary. Life happens to all of us. God "sends rain on the righteous and the unrighteous" (Matt. 5:45). Sometimes it's necessary to temporarily drop the pressures of life in order to celebrate a child's making her bed for the first time or a teen's getting his learner's permit. When we celebrate, we teach our kids to recognize God's blessings in the midst of everything else that is happening.

In spite of any problems and worries you may have as a parent, what is worth celebrating in your children's lives now?

There is so much to celebrate in your children's lives:
- The first day of school
- When the last baby tooth falls out
- Baptism
- Getting braces off (gum, popcorn, everything they were never supposed to eat)
- When someone does something without being asked
- A new pet
- The first time they read Scripture on their own
- Overcoming fear (a child sleeps with no night light; a teenager stays home by himself)
- The ability to learn
- The first time they share their faith with a friend
- Delights of nature
- Rainy days
- A new friend
- Their first chapter book
- The first dress-up event
- Getting a learner's permit
- The first date
- Acceptance to college
- Moving into the dorm
- Coming to know Christ!

In the previous list, check the things your family has already celebrated in your children's lives. If you missed something, it's never too late to celebrate!

Life happens on the way to doing something else.

Celebration says that as life happens—the good, the bad, and the ugly—we will intentionally choose to focus on the good. The other is not ignored. Life's stuff has to be addressed. Yet it will not drown out the celebration. As a family, resolve to periodically get off the worry-go-round and have some fun together.

CELEBRATION IN THE BIBLE

God's Word is full of celebration! In fact, God bookends the entire Bible with celebration. In Genesis, after the first week in history, God saw all He created and essentially said, "This is good stuff!" It was a moment of celebration.

Genesis 1:31
"God saw all that He had made, and it was very good."

Likewise, God's Word ends with the mother of all celebrations—a new heaven, a new earth, and a new Jerusalem with jewels for walls. Through the city runs a river of living water, and Jesus invites us to drink of it (see Rev. 21–22). Not your average party! When you teach your children about celebrations in God's Word, you remind them that we serve a God who loves to fill our hearts with joy. The celebrations in the world are cheap imitations of the richness of God's presence in our lives.

Following are some celebrations from Scripture that you can read and discuss with your children. Use the parenting points to guide your discussions. Notice that many parties happened in the midst of challenging times.

Jesus' first miracle—John 2
- The setting: a wedding feast
- The party planner: Jesus
- The party pooper: no more wine
- The celebration: Jesus turned water into wine. Why? So that the blind could see? So that lame people could walk? Nope. He'd do that later. For His very first miracle Jesus turned water into wine so that the celebration could continue!

- The parenting point: Sometimes God works and brings glory to Himself through the simple celebrations of life.

The return of the prodigal—Luke 15
- The setting: the home of a grieving Jewish father
- The party planner: the dad
- The party pooper: The younger son basically told his dad to drop dead, took his money, and squandered it.
- The celebration: The son came home! Talk about a party waiting to happen! The celebration centered on the son's return. No accomplishments. No job well done. No productivity. Just a celebration of life. The older brother didn't get it. The dad said to him, "We'll settle all other worries later. For now let's celebrate because your brother, who we thought was dead, is alive."
- The parenting point: God is like the father in this story. He loves us even when we don't love Him. When we return to Him, He rejoices and showers us with His blessings.

David dances before the ark of the Lord—2 Samuel 6
- The setting: Jerusalem, when the ark of the covenant, representing God's presence, returned to Israel
- The party planner: King David
- The party pooper: a killjoy wife
- The celebration: The ark was finally home, and David was beside himself. It was time to get happy. However, David's wife, Michal, clearly disapproved of his undignified display. Yet David declared, "I will celebrate before the LORD" (v. 21). Michal didn't receive the favor of the king even though he was her husband.
- The parenting point: The enemy tries to steal our joy. When we truly love God with all our heart, soul, mind, and strength, nothing can rob us of our desire to celebrate Him.

Select one of the previous examples to read and discuss with your children. How did they respond to the idea of celebrating God?

The psalmist gave us several examples of praise and celebration to God:

Celebration of God's Justice—Psalm 9:1-2, The Message
"I'm thanking you, GOD, from a full heart, I'm writing the book on your wonders. I'm whistling, laughing, and jumping for joy; I'm singing your song, High God."

Praise to the Creator—Psalm 33:1-3
"Rejoice in the LORD, you righteous ones; praise from the upright is beautiful. Praise the LORD with the lyre; make music to Him with a ten-stringed harp. Sing a new song to Him; play skillfully on the strings with a joyful shout."

Praise for the Lord's Works—Psalm 111:2-4
"The LORD's works are great, studied by all who delight in them. All that He does is splendid and majestic; His righteousness endures forever. He has caused His wonderful works to be remembered."

Praising God's Greatness—Psalm 145:1-5
"I exalt You, my God the King, and praise Your name forever and ever. I will praise You every day; I will honor Your name forever and ever. Yahweh is great and is highly praised; His greatness is unsearchable. One generation will declare Your works to the next and will proclaim Your mighty acts. I will speak of Your glorious splendor and Your wonderful works."

Your children learn how to celebrate by watching you. You get to declare God's mighty acts to your children. Read them stories from God's Word and tell them how He has worked in your life. Influence the next generation by bringing biblical accounts of Christ-centered celebration to life in your home.

"Children have more need of models than of critics."[1]—*Carolyn Coats*

If your family does not have regular family devotions, consider beginning this practice. You might start with the passages discussed in the previous section.

CELEBRATING OUTSIDE THE LINES

Celebrations aren't limited to the big things in life. Bring celebration into the ordinary patterns of family life, even if it means coloring outside the lines. To help our family think celebration, Selma created the party drawer—the bottom drawer of our antique buffet table—where she stored everything related to parties. Selma kept her eye open for sales and stocked the drawer with balloons, streamers, crayons, markers, scissors, paper plates, napkins, and so on. (Remember when we said the parent adventure can be messy?) Anyone in the family might declare, "It's time to celebrate"; and off we'd go to the party drawer.

How does your family celebrate in the middle of everyday life?

No matter what ages your children are, they can learn to interrupt the daily routine with celebration. Here are some ideas to get them started.
- *Preschool.* Play dress-up with old clothes. Put on an apron and help cook dinner. Display artwork around the house.
- *Elementary age.* Decorate the house. Make a surprise dinner for Mom and Dad. Invite the neighborhood children over for a party.
- *Preadolescent.* Invite friends over for a spend-the-night party just for fun. Host a makeup party. Eat pizza on the living-room floor.
- *Adolescent.* Celebrate surviving exams, participating in ministry, going out for a team, or touring colleges.
- *College age.* Celebrate finishing the first semester or year, deciding on a major, or going on a mission trip.

Even celebrations that happen in the middle of life can point your children to God. That doesn't mean every celebration has to include a Bible story and a prayer. It's more about creating an environment of celebration that becomes conducive to sharing truth about God. In the middle of every celebration, remind your children that God loves and rejoices over them. By celebrating, you model God's character and create opportunities to teach your children the joy of knowing Christ.

It is said that children laugh between 300 and 400 times a day. Adults average 15 times a day!

Celebrating attracts the world. When you start making a big deal about report cards, a missing tooth, and the longest day of the year, your children's friends and your neighbors will notice. The world sometimes sees Christians as stuffy, irrelevant, and solemn. Celebration shatters those misconceptions. Believers can be joyful, exciting, life-filled people who celebrate in a way that gets the world's attention. Don't be surprised if your celebration impacts your neighborhood, community, and city!

Name something ordinary in your family that you could celebrate.

Identify people you could involve who need to see a family that celebrates with the joy of Christ.

FINANCING THE FUN

Warning: Teaching your children to celebrate can be hazardous to your image! The girls once saved their money to buy me a surprise for no special reason. Dad took them shopping, but they got to pick the surprise for Mom on their own (Thanks, Honey.) They were so excited. They wrapped the gift themselves, and we had a special evening of celebration just for me.

After a simple meal of macaroni and cheese, they presented me the gift.
The girls anxiously hovered with eyes sparkling, unable to contain their excitement. To my ... er, surprise, they had gotten me a huge pair of bright yellow earrings— one in the shape of a question mark and the other an exclamation point! Yikes! Of course, I immediately put them on and had to wear them the next day!

Who would have ever thought a pair of earrings would be a tool I could use to share God with others? If someone noticed them, I could tell about our girls; our family; and ultimately, our faith in God, who gives us so many reasons to celebrate.

Name a special gift from your children that didn't cost a great deal of money but was very special to you. What made it special?

Ever heard the expression "It's the thought that counts"? In a family celebration the thought is exactly what counts! Money is no object. Rather, money shouldn't be the object. For instance, when the girls were small, we celebrated report cards, reflecting on the ups and downs, the good and the bad of another six weeks. Often our celebrations were merely a means of giving our girls some major attention. Sometimes we'd just hang out in the living room, give a prayer of thanks, and express how proud we were of them. Other times we'd go to their favorite restaurant, play games, and eat too much pizza.

Our personal twist: the report-card celebration happened every six weeks regardless of their grades. In fact, the party was planned before they ever shared the results. We celebrated their hard work, their schools and teachers, and how God had blessed them with the ability and opportunity to learn.

Recall the reason to celebrate you identified on page 131. Describe an inexpensive but creative way you could celebrate.

The more creative you are, the less emphasis money will demand. How you celebrate can outweigh how much you spend celebrating. Granted, some celebrations will cost more than others, but don't make it about the money. Instead, make it about the recognition and the opportunity to teach your children about God in the moment. That's a party not to be missed!

CELEBRATING THROUGH THEIR EYES

Kids get excited over the craziest things. What brings them joy might not connect with you at all, but that's OK. Whether or not it affects you personally, sometimes you just need to celebrate anyway.

"You don't really understand human nature unless you know why a child on a merry-go-round will wave at his parents every time around—and why his parents will always wave back."[2]—*William D. Tammeus*

When Natalie was six years old, I missed the first game of a softball doubleheader but arrived between games. She saw me and with unlimited jubilation exclaimed, all in one breath, "Oh, Daddy, this is so much fun. I've struck out five times. I love playing softball!" We'd work on Natalie's swing later, but at that moment I hugged her and shared her excitement.

Recently, Natalie, now grown up and completing a medical internship in another city, called to share another unique accomplishment: "Dad, today I got to work with the doctors in the GI lab. I saw seven colonoscopies this morning. It was awesome!" Once again, it didn't add up to me; but I knew it was time to celebrate!

Think of a time when one of your children was excited about something that seemed mundane or strange to you. How did you react?

☐ Ignored him or her   ☐ Celebrated with him or her
☐ Put him or her down   ☐ Told him or her to grow up
☐ Other:

Identify something your family could celebrate in your child's life. Describe a way the celebration could be planned and expressed through your child's eyes.

CELEBRATING CHANGE

In chapter 3, "A Yes Home," we stated that parents' natural response toward their kids' strange ideas is usually no. In Christ we can rewire that default setting so that we say yes when possible. The same is true of change. An adult's natural response to change is to say no. As parents, we often cling to our children's current age, grieve its passing and gloomily dread the coming stage. But change is inevitable when we have children. Besides the Lord Himself (see Heb. 13:8), change is the only constant this life offers. When we have an attitude of celebration, we can welcome change in our children's lives.

Hebrews 13:8
"Jesus Christ is the same yesterday, today, and forever."

Dealing with change is one of the most valuable lessons we can teach our children. Parents who celebrate life changes portray a future-focused outlook on life: "We're excited about your going into kindergarten" or "It's going to be awesome having a 13-year-old in our home!" (Really? Yes, really!) Such encouragement can help kids anticipate what lies ahead for them instead of dreading it.

On the other hand, guys and girls can feel guilty when we tell them, "You're not my baby anymore," "I wish you were still little so that I could hold you as I used to," or "Oh, no, we're going to have a teenager in the house!" These comments sound as if parents are blaming the child for growing up.

During our young parenting days we often sought counsel and wisdom from our friends, the Byrums, whose kids were five or six years older than Jennifer and Natalie. At one point Selma asked Faye, the mom, "How do you handle your kids leaving one phase and growing into another?" Her response became our mantra: "It's not really that hard. We just look at each phase as better than the one before."

These parents celebrated the change in their children's lives. We immediately claimed a similar attitude for our parenting, telling our girls that their current stage of life was the best stage yet. And it was, partly because we determined in advance to make it that way. The girls are grown now, but we still celebrate where they are in their lives. It's still the best stage yet! And grandchildren have yet to arrive!

I remember telling the girls when they were 9 or 10, "Do I miss that toddler running around whom I could pick up and carry anywhere? Sometimes, but I wouldn't trade the times we have together now and the level of conversation we have now for anything! It's the best time yet!"

Name each of your children and state one thing that is great about his or her stage of life.

Certain passages children go through are more challenging than others. When they go through puberty, for example, complete with body changes, voice changes, and attitude changes, insecurities can skyrocket. Often they do not like what is happening in their lives. Yet there is good in every stage your children enter. When a parent says, "I am glad you are at this age. I wouldn't want you to be at any other stage than where you are right now," it can be a drink of cold water in the desert of preadolescence. A simple, encouraging statement can literally recharge your preteen's self-esteem.

Encourage your children this week by telling them the things you identified in the previous activity.

> "If you want your children to improve, let them overhear the nice things you say about them to others."[3]—*Haim Ginott*

Not all change is fun and games. Can change be painful? Absolutely! Telling high-school classmates good-bye on graduation night is not easy. But parents get to help their children see that God works in the change for good, whether or not we understand it at the time. Whether your kid is learning to take his own bath or is saying good-bye to his first-grade teacher at the end of the year, parents can teach that God is always working through the changes occurring in their kids' lives.

God has promised to bring good in all things for those who love Him: "We know that all things work together for the good of those who love God: those who are called according to His purpose" (Rom. 8:28). *All things* means all things! Even when the changes in your childrens lives are not pleasant, God works in them for their good. God's Word assures us that at whatever stage we find the parent-kid relationship, it is good in God's eyes. Look for it. Find it. Point it out to your kid. Ask God to open your eyes to find the good in every difficult situation. In doing so, you will teach your children always to seek God's perspective on their circumstances.

What are some changes your children face now?

How do you feel about these changes? Check all that apply.

☐ Afraid   ☐ Insecure   ☐ Confident   ☐ Hopeful   ☐ Despondent
☐ Excited   ☐ Other:

Do you see anything good that could come from these changes? If so, what?

Take time to pray about each change, asking God to give you a positive perspective so that you can encourage your children and can show them ways God is working in their lives.

TEACHING SPIRITUAL TRUTH AS YOU GO

One time God used celebration to drive home a profound spiritual truth in our youngest daughter, Natalie. I mentioned in a previous chapter that my mother died of cancer. During the last week of her life, while Jennifer was away at a girls camp, Natalie, seven, and I went to spend time with Mom. She was confined to bed, and her body was frail, but we had many precious moments during that week.

As I prepared to leave her for what would be the last time, I kissed Mom good-bye and can still feel her smile and whisper of "I love you." Early the next morning Rodney and I were asleep when the call came. Mom had died peacefully in the early hours of the morning.

I was crying, and Natalie must have heard us talking because she came into our room and crawled into bed with us. We held her and told her about Nana. Then she slipped out of bed and went into another room. I wasn't sure what she was doing, but soon she came back with a picture she had drawn. She handed me the picture and said with a big smile, "Mommy, Nana is in heaven now running and playing, see?" The picture was of a big party, complete with a welcome banner, balloons, and streamers. That picture stayed on the refrigerator for a long time (like all great works of art by my children) and remains in our memories as a constant reminder of why we celebrate.

The greatest celebration centers on God's love for us. He loved us so much that He sent His one and only Son to die for us (see John 3:16). We can have abundant life through Jesus (see John 10:10). We get eternal life because of Jesus! God created us, Jesus died for us, and God sent His Spirit to live in us. Celebration? You bet! Luke 15:10 says, "There is joy in the presence of God's angels over one sinner who repents." I'm pretty sure heaven knows how to throw a party.

Read the Scriptures below, which state reasons you and your kids have to celebrate. Match each reference with the correct promise for your children.

  ___ 1. Genesis 1:27   a. Your children were created in God's image.

  ___ 2. Isaiah 40:28-29   b. God loves your children so much
             that He died for them.

  ___ 3. John 3:16   c. God will give your children strength.

Genesis 1:27

"God created man in His own image; He created him in the image of God; He created them male and female."

Isaiah 40:28-29

"Do you not know? Have you not heard? Yahweh is the everlasting God, the Creator of the whole earth. He never grows faint or weary; there is no limit to His understanding. He gives strength to the weary and strengthens the powerless."

John 3:16

"God loved the world in this way: He gave His One and Only Son, so that everyone who believes in Him will not perish but have eternal life."

Let's end our study by looking again at the core verse for this study:

Deuteronomy 6:5-7

"Love the LORD your God with all your heart, with all your soul, and with all your strength. These words that I am giving you today are to be in your heart. Repeat them to your children. Talk about them when you sit in your house and when you walk along the road, when you lie down and when you get up."

Celebrate God's work and His blessings with your children—all God is, all He has given us, and all He has yet to do in our lives. Truly, there is much to celebrate. Remind your children of that as you go through life with them.

FROM **LIFEWAY RESEARCH**

The most common definitions parents have for *SUCCESS* are if their kids—

25%

- grow up to have good values (25 percent);
- are happy (25 percent);
- are successful in life (22 percent);
- are good people (19 percent);
- get a college degree (17 percent);
- are independent adults (15 percent).[4]

THE PARENT ADVENTURE PLAN

What are three things you can celebrate with your children this week?

1.

2.

3.

What can you tell your children about God's work in your life that causes you to celebrate?

Find a verse in God's Word to express your celebration of God. Select one from this chapter if you wish.

PRAYER FOCUS

Father, I praise You. You are glorious and wonderful. The works of Your hands amaze and astound me. I celebrate even now the work of salvation You have brought to my life. Father, help me teach my children to celebrate life because of You. May they see in me the wonder of You. I pray that my children will know You and surrender to You.

THE
ADVENTURE
CONTINUES

epilogue

THE ADVENTURE CONTINUES
epilogue

 ## GET TO KNOW YOUR GROUP

DISCUSS what you discovered from your parent adventure after reading chapter 6, "Celebrate!"

 ## WATCH DVD

- Watch DVD session 7.
- What stood out to you in this session?

 ## THE BIBLICAL VIEW

Hebrews 12:1
"Run with endurance the race that lies before us."

 ## THE ADVENTURE

As your adventure continues, what do you want from your parenting experience? What do you think God wants to accomplish through you and your family? What are you looking for?

 ## CLOSING THOUGHTS

Share ways this study has motivated and prepared you to be a better parent and to approach parenting as a great adventure.

One of our family's favorite authors is C. S. Lewis. In the final scene of *The Lion, the Witch, and the Wardrobe,* the Pevensie children have just returned from an exhilarating array of adventures in Narnia and have found their way back to the professor's house. They ask the professor, "Will we ever return to Narnia?" He assures them that although traveling through the wardrobe might be over, many more adventures await them in Narnia.

Wherever you are on this parent adventure, we assure you that many more adventures await you. Exciting? Absolutely! Dangerous? Often. But God, who is the author, giver, and adventure of life, will be with you on all of them. Trust in Him. Rest in Him. Run to Him.

In John 1 Jesus noticed two men following Him. He turned and, typically, asked a thought-provoking question: "What are you looking for?" (v. 38). Throughout this study we have encouraged you to include God in your parenting, to talk with Him and seek His guidance in every aspect of your parenting experience, from the "Thank You, Lord. This is going great right now" to the "Help me, Lord, I think I'm going crazy with this 13-year-old!" and everything in between. What if He asked you, "What are you looking for in your parent adventure?" How would you respond?

As your children leave for their own adventures with God, your life as a parent is far from over. You may be tempted to recline in that easy chair or collapse on the couch for a much-needed rest (OK, a short nap is acceptable). The truth is that God has many more adventures awaiting you. Here is one parent's story.

> When I was 17, I felt God calling me to missions. My husband and I married almost five years later. We were both busy serving in churches and time went by. We went to a missionary appointment service for some friends going to Thailand to serve. During the service, I felt God saying, "Now is the time." I told God I couldn't go now because my baby (he was 22) needed me, and God told me clearly that He would take care of my son. I thought, I can't go now, Lord; my parents are close to 80. God told me again that He would take care of my parents better than I could. About that time, my husband said to me, "It's time." We stepped out on faith and almost to the date, one year later, we were appointed to the mission field to serve in Tanzania."[1]

We've encouraged you to form a game plan, an intentional strategy as you experience the adventure of parenting. But right now before you make any further plans for today or tomorrow, seek God. Ask Him to shape your parenting dreams and expectations. Let all your plans begin with Him. Wherever you are in your parenting—just beginning with a newborn, in the trenches (and joys) of the teen years, or on the verge of launching your children from the home—seek the Lord.

Take comfort in knowing that the adventure of parenting, with its battles, its challenges, and its responsibilities, is not yours alone. God (the Ultimate Parent) has promised never to leave you (see Heb. 13:5). His Son taught us that "with God all things are possible" (Matt. 19:26). Whatever you do or plan to do in your parent adventure, commit it to the Lord and watch Him work (see Prov. 3:16). That will be worth celebrating!

Hebrews 13:5

"He Himself has said, I will never leave you or forsake you."

Proverbs 16:3, NIV

"Commit to the LORD whatever you do, and your plans will succeed."

Thank you for investing this time with us. Let the parent adventure continue! We began this study with Paul's prayer in Ephesians 1:17-19 (see p. 26). We want to close our time together with another of Paul's prayers found in Ephesians 3:

Ephesians 3:16-21

"I pray that He may grant you, according to the riches of His glory, to be strengthened with power through His Spirit in the inner man and that the Messiah may dwell in your hearts through faith, I pray that you, being rooted and firmly established in love, may be able to comprehend with all the saints what is the breadth and width, height and depth of God's love, and to know the Messiah's love that surpasses knowledge, so that you may be filled with all the fullness of God. Now to Him who is able to do above and beyond all that we ask or think—according to the power that works in you—to Him be glory in the church and in Christ Jesus to all generations, forever and ever. Amen."

NOTES

CHAPTER 1

1. Alison Lutz and Dean Borgman, "Teen Spirituality and the Internet," International Cultic Studies Association [online], 2008 [cited 19 August 2008]. Available from the Internet: *www.icsahome.com/infoserv_articles/lutz_alison_teenagespiritualityandinternet.htm*.
2. John C. Bruhn, *The Sociology of Community Connections* [online], 2005 [cited 13 August 2008], 6. Available from the Internet: *books.google.com*.
3. "The Future of Happiness" [online], 2008 [cited 13 August 2008]. Available from the Internet: *www.socialtechnologies.com/mtv.aspx*.
4. "LifeWay Research Parenting Study," 2007–8.
5. Ibid.
6. Dave Barry, *Dave Barry's Guide to Life* (New York: Random House, 1991).
7. "LifeWay Research Parenting Study," 2007–8.

CHAPTER 2

1. Blake Segal [online], 2008 [cited 5 September 2008]. Available from the Internet: *www.jimpoz.com/quotes/Speaker:Blake_Segal*.
2. Tim Elmore. "Nurturing the Leader with Your Child" [online] n.d. [cited 20 August 2008]. Available from the Internet: *www.greekmovement.com/leadership/?p=19*.
3. Jonathan Edwards, *The Works of Jonathan Edwards*, vol. 1 (Peabody, MA: Hendrickson Publishers, 1998).
4. Jim Elliot [online], 2008 [cited 5 September 2008]. Available from the Internet: *www.wheaton.edu/bgc/archives/faq/20.htm*.
5. Fred Rogers, as quoted by Susan Ginsberg, *Family Wisdom* (New York: Columbia University Press, 1996).
6. "LifeWay Research Parenting Study," 2007–8.

CHAPTER 3

1. Shinichi Suzuki [online], n.d. [cited 5 September 2008]. Available from the Internet: *en.thinkexist.com/quotes/Shinichi_Suzuki*.
2. P. D. James [online], 2006 [cited 5 September 2008]. Available from the Internet: *www.thinkexist.com*.
3. Patti Davis, as quoted by Dahlia Porter and Gabriel Cervantes, *All About Dad* (Cincinnati: Adams Media, 2007).
4. "LifeWay Research Parenting Study," 2007–8.

CHAPTER 4

1. O. A. Battista [online], 2005 [cited 5 September 2008]. Available from the Internet: *motivationempire.com/inspirational_authors.php?page=1&author=O.%20A.%20Battista*.
2. "LifeWay Research Parenting Study," 2007–8.
3. Perry McGuire, "Buzz About 'the Talk,' " *HomeLife*, 46–47, November 2007.
4. Yogi Berra [online], 2008 [cited 5 September 2008]. Available from the Internet: *www.brainyquote.com/quotes/authors/y/yogi_berra.html*.
5. Lane Olinghouse [online], 2008 [cited 5 September 2008]. Available from the Internet: *quotegarden.com/parents.html*.
6. Laurence Steinberg, *You and Your Adolescent* (Bloomington, IN: Collins Living, 1997).
7. David and Vera Mace, conference.
8. "LifeWay Research Parenting Study," 2007–8.

CHAPTER 5

1. Robert A. Heinlein [online], 2008 [cited 5 September 2008]. Available from the Internet: *www.brainyquote.com/quotes/authors/r/robert_a_heinlein.html*.
2. Robert Lewin [online] n.d. [cited 5 September 2008]. Available from the Internet: *en.thinkexist.com/quotes/roger_lewin*.
3. Tony Dungy with Nathan Whitaker, *Quiet Strength* (Carol Stream, IL: Tyndale House, 2007), 213.
4. "LifeWay Research Parenting Study," 2007–8.

CHAPTER 6

1. Carolyn Coats [online] 2006 [cited 5 September 2008]. Available from the Internet: *www.worldofquotes.com/author/Carolyn-Coats/1/index.html*.
2. William D. Tammeus [online], 2006 [cited 5 September 2008]. Available from the Internet: *en.thinkexist.com/quotes/william_d._tammeus*.
3. Haim Ginott [online], 2008 [cited 5 September 2008]. Available from the Internet: *www.brainyquote.com/quotes/authors/h/haim_ginott.html*.
4. "LifeWay Research Parenting Study," 2007–8.

EPILOGUE

1. Nan Williams, in Judi S. Hayes, *Youth on Mission*, vol. 14 (Birmingham: Woman's Missionary Union, 2008), 50.

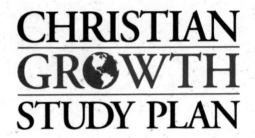

CHRISTIAN GROWTH STUDY PLAN

In the Christian Growth Study Plan *The Parent Adventure* is a resource for course credit in the subject area Personal Life in the Christian Growth category of plans. To receive credit, read the book; complete the learning activities; attend group sessions; show your work to your pastor, a staff member, or a church leader; then complete this form. This page may be duplicated. Send the completed form to:

Christian Growth Study Plan
One LifeWay Plaza; Nashville, TN 37234-0117
Fax (615) 251-5067; e-mail *cgspnet@lifeway.co*
For information about the Christian Growth Study
Plan, refer to the current *Christian Growth Study P*
Catalog, located online at *www.lifeway.com/cgsp.* If
do not have access to the Internet, contact the Chri
Growth Study Plan office, (800) 968-5519, for the spe
plan you need.

The Parent Adventure
COURSE NUMBER: 1424

PARTICIPANT INFORMATION

Social Security Number (USA ONLY-optional) | Personal CGSP Number* | Date of Birth (MONTH, DAY, YEAR)

Name (First, Middle, Last) | Home Phone

Address (Street, Route, or P.O. Box) | City, State, or Province | Zip/Postal Code

Email Address for CGSP use

Please check appropriate box: ❑ Resource purchased by church ❑ Resource purchased by self ❑ Other

CHURCH INFORMATION

Church Name

Address (Street, Route, or P.O. Box) | City, State, or Province | Zip/Postal Code

CHANGE REQUEST ONLY

❑ Former Name

❑ Former Address | City, State, or Province | Zip/Postal Code

❑ Former Church | City, State, or Province | Zip/Postal Code

Signature of Pastor, Conference Leader, or Other Church Leader | Date

*New participants are requested but not required to give SS# and date of birth. Existing participants, please give CGSP# when using SS# for the first time.
Thereafter, only one ID# is required. **Mail to:** Christian Growth Study Plan, One LifeWay Plaza, Nashville, TN 37234-0117. Fax: (615)251-5067.   Re